HK SPORT SCIENCE MONOGRAPH SERIES
Volume 5

Kinanthropometry in Aquatic Sports

A Study of World Class Athletes

J.E. Lindsay Carter, PhD
San Diego State University

Timothy R. Ackland, PhD
University of Western Australia
Editors

Juan C. Mazza and William D. Ross
Consulting Editors

Human Kinetics

Library of Congress Cataloging-in-Publication Data

Kinanthropometry in aquatic sports : a study of world class athletes /
  [edited by] J.E. Lindsay Carter, Timothy R. Ackland.
        p.   cm. -- (HK sport science monograph series, ISSN 0894-4229
  ; v. 5)
    Includes bibliographical references.
    ISBN 0-87322-658-5
    1. Aquatic sports--Physiological aspects. 2. Athletes-
Anthropometry. 3. Kinesiology.   I. Carter, J. E. L. (J. E.
Lindsay) II. Ackland, Timothy, R., 1958- .   III. Series.
RC1220.A65K56   1994
612'.044--dc20   93-42157
                                                                         CIP

ISBN: 0-87322-658-5
ISSN: 0894-4229

Copyright © 1994 by Human Kinetics Publishers, Inc.

Acquisitions Editors: Rick Frey, PhD
Developmental Editor: Larret Galasyn-Wright
Assistant Editors: Sally Bayless, Jacqueline Blakley, Matt Scholz, John Wentworth
Copyeditor: Margaret Darragh
Proofreader: Kathy Bennett
Typesetter: Angela K. Snyder
Text Designer: Keith Blomberg
Layout Artist: Tara Welsch, Denise Lowry, and Denise Peters
Cover Designer: Jody Boles
Printer: United Graphics

Printed in the United States of America

10 9 8 7 6 5 4 3 2 1

Human Kinetics
P.O. Box 5076, Champaign, IL 61825-5076
1-800-747-4457

Canada: Human Kinetics, Box 24040,
Windsor, ON N8Y 4Y9
1-800-465-7301 (in Canada only)

Europe: Human Kinetics, P.O. Box IW14,
Leeds LS16 6TR, England
0532-781708

Australia: Human Kinetics, P.O. Box 80,
Kingswood 5062, South Australia
618-374-0433

New Zealand: Human Kinetics, P.O. Box 105-231,
Auckland 1
(09) 309-2259

Contents

Contributors

Timothy R. Ackland
The University of Western Australia, Perth, Australia

Timothy M. Bach
Latrobe University, Victoria, Australia

J.E. Lindsay Carter
San Diego State University, San Diego, CA, USA

Patricia Cosolito
Biosystem, Rosario, Argentina

Julie Draper
Australia Sports Commission, Canberra, Australia

Donald T. Drinkwater
University of Saskatchewan Saskatoon, SK, Canada

Deborah A. Kerr
The University of Western Australia, Perth, Australia

Rob M. Leahy
Camosun College, Victoria, Canada

Michael J. Marfell-Jones
Central Institute of Technology, Trentham, New Zealand

Barbara A. Maslen
The University of Western Australia, Perth, Australia

Juan C. Mazza
Biosystem, Rosario, Argentina

William D. Ross
Simon Fraser University, Burnaby, Canada

HK Sport Science Monograph Series

The *HK Sport Science Monograph Series* is another endeavor to provide a useful communication channel for recording extensive research programs by sport scientists. Many publishers have discontinued publishing monographs because they have proven uneconomical. It is my hope that with the cooperation of authors, the use of electronic support systems, and the purchase of these monographs by sport scientists and libraries we can continue this series over the years.

The series will publish original research reports and reviews of literature that are sufficiently extensive not to lend themselves to reporting in available research journals. Subject matter pertinent to both the broad fields of the sport sciences and to physical education are considered appropriate for the monograph series, especially research in

- sport biomechanics,
- sport physiology,
- motor behavior (including motor control and learning, motor development, and adapted physical activity),
- sport psychology,
- sport sociology, and
- sport pedagogy.

Other titles in this series are:

- Adolescent Growth and Motor Performances: A Longitudinal Study of Belgian Boys
- Biological Effects of Physical Activity
- Growth and Fitness of Flemish Girls: The Leuven Growth Study
- Athletes and the American Hero Dilemma

Authors who wish to publish in the monograph series should submit two copies of the complete manuscript to the publisher. All manuscripts must conform to the current *APA Publication Manual* and be of a length between 120 and 300 doublespaced manuscript pages. The manuscript will be sent to two reviewers who will follow a review process similar to that used for scholarly journals. The decision with regard to the manuscript's acceptability will be based on its judged contribution to knowledge and on economic feasibility. Publications that are accepted, after all required revisions are made, must be submitted to the publisher on computer disk for electronic transfer to typesetting. No royalties will be paid for monographs published in this series.

Authors wishing to submit a manuscript to the monograph series or desiring further information should write to: Monograph Editor, Human Kinetics, Box 5076, Champaign, IL 61825 for further details.

Rainer Martens

Preface

Evaluating the relationships between physical structure and human performance is one of the goals of kinanthropometry. At the top level of performance, certain physiques are found more often in some sports than in others. Although several investigators have examined these relationships in international-level male and female swimming and male water polo, there are large gaps in our knowledge. There is also little information on elite diving and synchronized swimming or on women's water polo at any level of competition. The Sixth World Championships in swimming, diving, synchronized swimming, and water polo (held in Perth, Western Australia, January 1991) provided a unique opportunity to gain further knowledge of the physiques of athletes in these sports.

This book provides an overview of basic descriptive and comparative analyses of each sport, with analyses limited to simple breakdowns by sport, gender, event, place in the competition, and playing position. The results are intended to give preliminary descriptions and to provide a structural basis for exploring the biomechanical and physiological relevance of some aspects of physique to performance. To this end also separate analyses only are given for males and females within each sport; we have not attempted to look at sexual dimorphism, differences between sports, or other ways of classifying performance. More detailed questions and more sophisticated analyses will be addressed in future publications and presentations.

This single monograph covers all four sports; the reader interested in a single sport can select the appropriate sections to obtain all the relevant findings. All readers are encouraged to read the introduction and the first chapter to understand the purposes and execution of the project. If you need more information on the technical details of data collection, read chapter 2 and Appendixes A and B. To find out about the absolute size, somatotype, relative size, and body composition of the athletes in a sport, read the introduction and the appropriate sections about that sport in each of chapters 3 through 7. References are compiled in a single list; citations are limited primarily to studies of national- and international-level athletes that have used similar kinanthropometric approaches. The references are not meant to be exhaustive, nor are they critically examined in light of the present findings.

We have written *Kinanthropometry in Aquatic Sports* for the exercise scientist, coach, sport physician, athlete, or sport enthusiast who wants information on the physiques of world-class athletes in swimming, diving, synchronized swimming, or water polo.

Acknowledgments

Significant financial contributions for the Kinanthropometric Aquatic Sports Project were supplied by the Australian Sports Commission, the Western Australian Ministry of Sport and Recreation, the Exceed Sports Nutritionals Company, and the Department of Human Movement Studies at the University of Western Australia. The scientific committee wishes to express its gratitude to these generous institutions. Moreover, the committee is indebted to those members of the measurement team who, through their own institutions, financed some portion of their travel and equipment costs.

We also wish to thank sincerely the following groups of volunteer researchers and assistants who brought their wealth of experience from North America, Europe, Australia, and New Zealand. The execution of this project was due largely to their enthusiasm and dedication.

Anthropometrists: Tony Barbaro, Amanda Clough, Kay Cox, Sam Fazio, Enid Ginn, Julie Halbert, Andrew Hills, Kaylene Hood, Deborah Kerr, Michael Marfell-Jones, Jo Mitchell, Karen Monson, Ted Polglaze, Jordi Porta, Penny Rogers, Carolina Roser, Andrea Schreiner, Tanya Takayama, Anthea Walker, Rebecca Whitehead, Nancy Whittingham.

Support Staff and Recorders: Jenny Ackland, Tony Ames, Lisa Chivers, Rick Ellis, Ann Gibson, Joanne Gibson, Sarah Gibson, Sue Malcolm, Nicola Maslen, Carolyn McKee, Natalie Mrachacz, Geoff Sweeney, Christine Taylor, Marcus Wilkinson.

Finally, the success of this project would not have been possible without the cooperation of the athletes (919 in all), coaches, physicians, and officials with the delegations. To all of them we extend our sincere thanks.

Introduction

Timothy R. Ackland and Juan C. Mazza

Athletes, coaches, sport scientists, and physical educators are interested in knowledge of the structure and function of the human body, especially in relation to athletic performance. Since the 1920s several studies have focused on physical and physiological factors that might contribute to success for elite athletes in a variety of sports. Some of these studies have involved aquatic athletes; although they elicit several important findings, much of the material is outdated, is limited in scope, or was analyzed by a variety of incompatible methodologies. Thus there is a need for a current description and comparison of the physical structure of world-class competitors in swimming, diving, synchronized swimming, and water polo. Such a project would help us understand the biomechanical and physiological ramifications of modern training methods, the optimum physique for successful participation, and determine selection criteria for the identification of talented junior competitors.

Kinanthropometry is defined as the quantitative interface between human structure and function. This interface is examined through the measurement and analysis of age, body size, shape, proportion, composition, and maturation as they relate to gross body function. It provides a coherent rationale for the study of physique and physical performance, monitoring change and assessing structural constraints that may affect performance or relate to health or well-being (Ross, De Rose, & Ward, 1988).

Related Research

No kinanthropometric studies have been made on swimmers at the World Championships, but the few conducted at the Olympic Games are reported in several books (Carter, 1982a, 1984a; Cureton, 1951; de Garay, Levine, & Carter, 1974; Jungmann, 1976). These studies have provided fruitful information on the physiques of aquatic athletes, but low sample sizes reduce their effectiveness (Table 1). Morphological differences between swimmers and other athletes have been reported in these investigations of Olympic competitors and elsewhere in studies by Brief (1986); Hebbelinck, Carter, and de Garay (1975); Rodriguez, Sanchez, Garcia, Martinez, and Cabrera (1986); Thorland, Johnson, Fagot, Tharp, and Hammer (1981); and Withers, Craig, and Norton (1986). Relationships between swimming performance and physique have also been reported for a variety of performance levels by Araujo, Pavel, and Gomes (1978); Bale (1986); Bloomfield,

Blanksby, Ackland, and Elliott (1986); Mazza et al. (1991b); Stager, Cordain, and Becker (1984); Tittel and Wutscherk (1972); Vervaeke and Persyn (1981). In general, the findings from these studies show that swimmers possess well-defined physical characteristics. Moreover, they differ from athletes in other sports, their physiques change with age and training, a secular trend in physique is evident between present and past swimmers, and there are structural differences with varying levels of competition. Differences in morphology between various event and distance specialists have not been clearly defined, though, due in part to small sample sizes.

A few studies on the morphology of elite divers have been reported (Carter, 1984a; de Garay et al., 1974; Hebbelinck et al., 1975; Rodriguez et al., 1986); their results suggest a body structure more akin to gymnasts than to swimmers.

Only three studies report on structural characteristics of elite synchronized swimmers (Hawes & Sovak, 1992; Kirkendall, Delio, Hagerman, & Fox, 1982; Ross, Marfell-Jones, & Stirling, 1982), none of which were performed at a World Championship event. Evidence from these studies suggests a difference in morphology between swimmers and synchronized swimmers, with synchronized swimmers demonstrating more variability.

The data on male international water polo players are limited to studies at the 1968 and 1972 Olympics (Carter, 1984a; de Garay et al., 1974; Hebbelinck et al., 1975; Novak, Bestit, Mellerowicz, & Woodward, 1976a). Male water polo players are generally taller, heavier, and more mesomorphic than swimmers; however, many structural characteristics remain common for both types of athletes. There are no studies on female players.

Table 1   Sample Sizes From Previous Studies on Physiques of Aquatic Athletes at the International Level of Competition

Aquatic sport	Gender	Mexico[a] Olympics 1968	Munich[b] Olympics 1972	Montreal[c] Olympics 1976
Swimming	Female	32	—	32
	Male	67	14	33
Diving	Female	7	—	1
	Male	17	—	4
Synchronized swimming	Female	—	—	—
Water polo	Female	—	—	—
	Male	71	10	3

[a]de Garay et al. (1974), [b]Novak et al. (1976a, 1976b), [c]Carter (1982a; 1984a).

Significance of the Study

Review of related research indicates clearly that no description of the morphology of world-ranking aquatic athletes existed before the present study. Therefore, the successful measurement of a large sample could provide important information for coaches and athletes, which could be used as normative data throughout the 1990s.

Physical Characteristics of World-Class Competitors

Much of this book is devoted to the provision of descriptive data for physical characteristics of participants in various aquatic events. Evidence suggests that changes in the training and preparation of aquatic athletes over the last two decades have resulted in corresponding changes in the optimal physique. Thus results from the small data samples measured at previous Olympic Games are probably outdated and of limited value for selecting and preparing aquatic athletes today. Chapters 3 through 6 provide normative data for variables related to absolute body size, somatotype, relative body size, and body composition, divided by gender in swimming, diving, synchronized swimming, and water polo. The large sample permitted further breakdown within sports, where physical characteristics were identified for athletes in the different events in a particular sport.

Optimum Physique

In addition to normative data based on all athletes who competed and were measured at the World Championships, we identify those characteristics that distinguish the successful performers from the lower ranked athletes. Thus, a portion of chapters 3 through 6 describes the optimal physique for success in events within four aquatic sports.

Selection Criteria for Talent Development

Many age-group swimmers and divers decide to specialize in a particular aquatic sport or event based on a number of factors. Most probably would not consider the advantages or disadvantages afforded by their body structure and composition when choosing to specialize in a sport. This comes as no surprise, because there has been little objective data from which to make such a decision.

We hope that with the data from this project structural characteristics, which are critical for success at the international level of competition, may be identified for the various events and used for talent identification and development. This is of great importance for young athletes and helps to prevent their disenchantment if pursuing success in an event for which they do not possess the optimal physical attributes.

Chapter 1

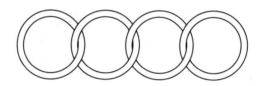

Organization Procedures and Sample

Timothy R. Ackland, Barbara A. Maslen, and Julie Draper

During the Sixth Fédération Internationale de Natation Amateur (International Federation of Amateur Swimming) (FINA) World Championships of Swimming, Diving, Synchronized Swimming, and Water Polo held in Perth, Western Australia in January 1991, an international team of researchers undertook anthropological investigations on elite aquatic athletes. This project, named KASP (the Kinanthropometric Aquatic Sports Project), represented the culmination of 2 years of organization and lobbying by the scientific committee. Dr. Juan C. Mazza of Argentina made the initial proposal to the FINA Medical Committee in Seoul in 1988 and was encouraged to submit a more detailed proposal at the next meeting in London in 1989. These attempts to gain approval and financial support from FINA were unsuccessful, so the scientific committee turned to colleagues in Australia for help. Following commitments from the Australian Sports Commission and the University of Western Australia, the approval of the FINA Medical Committee, the World Championships organizing committee, and the Australian aquatic sports federations was received by September 1990. A submission to the Human Rights Committee of the University of Western Australia was accepted in November 1990.

Personnel

A scientific committee (Timothy R. Ackland, University of Western Australia; Juan C. Mazza, Biosystem, Argentina; J.E. Lindsay Carter, San Diego State University, USA; and William D. Ross, Simon Fraser University, Canada) was responsible for all the financial and administrative functions of KASP and for overseeing the eventual publication of data. Technical and scientific support was provided by Don Drinkwater, University of Manitoba, Canada; Tim Bach, Latrobe University, Australia; Deborah Kerr, University of Western Australia; Julie Draper, Australian Sports Commission; and Barbara Maslen, University of Western Australia.

The training of local anthropometrists began in Perth in September 1990, under the guidance of Ross and Kerr. Although the testers had prior experience as anthropometrists, training sessions were essential to ensure that measurements were standardized and that testers were reliable and accurate (see Appendix B). Kerr was appointed the criterion anthropometrist for KASP, and a series of test–retest reliability sessions was conducted under her direction. Pilot testing under simulated laboratory conditions was also held in Perth in November 1990 with a group of Australian Masters swimmers and again in Wollongong, New South Wales, at the Australian swim team's training camp in December 1990. From December 27 to the end of testing, Carter and Marfell-Jones joined Kerr as criterion anthropometrists.

Facilities

Two laboratories, established to handle most of the data collection, were open from 8:00 a.m. until 6:00 p.m. 10 days before the competition through the last day of competition (December 22, 1990, to January 13, 1991). The main laboratory, situated within the Superdrome competition complex, offered athletes easy access during training and competition. All personnel were given limited access to the competition venue to facilitate their work at the laboratory; the three subject recruiters were accredited to all competition areas and to the media center for the collection of results. A second laboratory was established at the University of Western Australia's Department of Human Movement Studies and was strategically located near many participants' accommodations. With the added incentive for extra training afforded by the department's heated pools, the university laboratory was well used in the early stages of data collection.

A mobile laboratory, consisting of a 10-seat bus and portable equipment, was dispatched to accommodation venues and other field sites when no suitable schedule could be arranged for team testing at either of the main laboratories. This mobile laboratory proved highly successful, being used to measure over 200 subjects.

Recruitment of Subjects

Initial contact was made by mail with each competing federation in October 1990, inviting coaches, physicians, and athletes to participate in KASP (see Appendix A.1). A confirmation slip (returned by airmail or fax) named an officer who subject recruiters could approach upon the team's arrival. Secondary contact was made with coaches and team managers during prechampionship training sessions; testing appointments were scheduled into training, recreation, or event times. The difficult task of recruiting athletes was achieved successfully under the enthusiastic direction of Mazza with the assistance of Draper and Ackland.

Data Collection

A maximum of 15 subjects each hour could be measured at the laboratory; but data entry and report generation required more time, so individual reports were distributed the following day (see chapter 2). Upon entering the laboratory subjects were instructed to read and sign the statement of consent form (see Appendix A.2). Translated copies of the consent statement (in Spanish, French, and Chinese) were available, and with the assistance of the team liaison officers, an adequate explanation of the test session was made to all participants. Demographic data were then entered onto the data sheets (see Appendix A.2).

The subject, wearing a lightweight swimsuit only, was then landmarked by a criterion anthropometrist and sent to the measurement stations. Each station, composed of variables that required similar measurement equipment, maximized ergonomic efficiency and the use of time. Upon completion of the measures, the demographic data were encoded, data sheets were placed in the input queue for computer entry, and somatotype photographs were taken of the subject. Lastly, individual reports were produced and checked prior to distribution (see chapter 2 and Appendix A.2 and A.3).

Sample

Data were collected on 919 athletes, and individual performance information was then added to each subject's data file. With an estimated 1,050 athletes in attendance, those tested represented 88% of the competitor population, far exceeding previous samples for similar surveys. The large tally remains a tribute to the dedication of the volunteer staff and cooperation from the delegations.

Competing Nations

Competitors from 52 countries were measured in the KASP sample (see Table 1.1). Most competitors were from Europe, with the remainder largely from Australasia and North America. Europe included countries in Western and Eastern

Table 1.1   Geographic Origin of the Athletes

Region	Countries	Females	Males	Total	%
Europe	24	233	252	485	52.8
AUS & NZ[a]	3	82	61	143	15.5
CAN & USA	2	58	44	102	11.1
Asia	9	41	45	86	9.4
C & SA[b]	8	36	42	78	8.5
Middle East	5	4	19	23	2.5
Africa	1	1	1	2	0.2
Totals	52	455	464	919	100.0

[a]AUS & NZ = Australia and New Zealand, plus New Guinea; [b]C & SA = Mexico, Caribbean, and South America.

Europe. Middle Eastern participants came from Algeria, Egypt, Israel, Kuwait, and Turkey. The countries of Chinese Taipei, Guam, Hong Kong, Indonesia, Japan, Korea, Macao, People's Republic of China, and Singapore comprised the Asian group. The Australian, New Zealand, and New Guinea teams comprised Australasia, whereas only one African country, Zimbabwe, was included. Canada and the United States were grouped as North America; Mexico and countries further south were grouped as Central and South America.

Demographic Information

Most athletes in the KASP sample were Caucasian; Orientals were the next largest ethnic group (Table 1.2). The mean ages of the competitors (female = 20.9 yr, male = 23.0 yr) are higher than those measured in previous studies by Carter (1984a), de Garay et al. (1974), and Novak et al. (1976a, 1976b). These differences are especially pronounced when one considers the comparison of ages within sport categories. For example, the mean ages of KASP swimmers (female = 19.5 yr, male = 21.3) are about 2 years more than those reported for swimmers measured in previous Olympic Games projects.

Swimming

Table 1.3 shows the breakdown of competitors by gender and swimming event. The selection of primary event was based on the athlete's perception of his or her strongest event rather than on the eventual results. Further evidence of the quality of this sample may be seen under the table headings "Percent of total competitors" and "Percent of A and B finalists."

Table 1.2   Age and Race-Ethnicity of Athletes in Aquatic Sports

Race-ethnicity	N	M	SD[a]	Range[b]
Females				
White	389	21.1	3.5	11.4-32.6
Black	5	20.1	1.8	18.1-22.2
Mestizo	9	21.6	2.7	18.7-27.5
Oriental	38	19.0	2.3	12.4-24.3
Middle Eastern	3	20.4	2.4	18.2-22.9
Other	11	17.9	3.0	13.6-24.4
Totals	455	20.9	3.4	11.4-32.6
Males				
White	370	23.3	3.6	15.5-35.5
Black	12	22.6	4.1	17.8-30.3
Mestizo	13	24.5	4.2	17.7-30.2
Oriental	41	21.4	4.2	14.9-34.7
Middle Eastern	17	23.6	5.6	14.3-36.7
Other	11	16.8	2.4	13.1-19.9
Totals	464	23.0	3.9	13.1-36.7

[a]SD = standard deviation; [b]Range = range of ages.

For most swimming events 70% to 80% of all competitors were measured in KASP, with a similar or slightly higher percentage of A and B finalists measured in these groups. Many swimmers competed in more than one event, and some participated in relay teams as well. For the discussion of performance-related aspects of morphology in chapters 3 through 6, data from relay competitions were used only if the swimmer participated in no other event. In these cases, if the competitor swam the first leg of the relay, then the elapsed time was used to calculate a performance rank with respect to the elapsed times for other competitors in the equivalent primary event. For relay competitors who swam the second, third, or fourth legs, a constant 0.7 s was added to the elapsed time to account for the advantage afforded by a flying start. This method is consistent with the formula adopted to determine world rankings, according to Stuart Alldritt, Australian Records Officer (personal communication, March

Table 1.3   Sample of Swimmers by Gender and Competition Event

Gender	Event		1^a	2 or 3	Event total	Percent of total competitors	Percent of A & B finalists
Females	50	FR[b]	16	15	31	82	81
(N = 170)	100	FR	15	21	36	75	81
	200	FR	21	12	33	81	75
	400	FR	6	12	18	86	88
	800	FR	6	9	15	83	88
	50	BR	6	4	10	76	77
	100	BR	10	14	24	83	94
	200	BR	12	7	19	88	80
	50	BK	1	10	11	65	69
	100	BK	7	10	17	67	56
	200	BK	10	8	18	84	75
	50	FL	5	11	16	85	94
	100	FL	11	18	29	85	81
	200	FL	13	9	22	89	81
	200	IM	10	10	20	81	81
	400	IM	11	7	18	76	81
		LD	10	—	10	63	40
Males	50	FR	19	11	30	66	69
(N = 231)	100	FR	28	20	48	73	75
	200	FR	24	17	41	78	69
	400	FR	10	18	28	73	81
	1500	FR	10	7	17	77	88
	50	BR	8	7	15	69	79
	100	BR	17	11	28	70	50
	200	BR	12	13	25	74	56
	50	BK	6	9	15	68	81
	100	BK	9	19	28	74	69
	200	BK	13	12	25	74	75
	50	FL	5	16	21	71	88
	100	FL	19	18	37	82	73
	200	FL	17	8	35	71	67
	200	IM	10	18	28	69	63
	400	IM	11	10	21	76	69
		LD	13	—	13	48	40

[a]1 = primary event preference, 2 or 3 = secondary or tertiary event preference; [b]FR = freestyle, BR = breaststroke, BK = backstroke, FL = butterfly stroke, IM = individual medley, LD = 25-km long-distance swim.

1991), and was used only in less than 1% of cases. Also, note that the long-distance swimming event was a 25-km swim in open water—Swan River in Perth.

Diving

Table 1.4 shows the breakdown of diving competitors by gender and event. Once again, the athlete's perception determined the selection of primary event, rather than the basis being the eventual results. A very high proportion of all competitors as well as the top 10 competitors were measured.

Synchronized Swimming

Table 1.5 shows the breakdown of competitors (females only) by synchronized swimming event. The Solo category included all competitors entered in this event; the Duet category included competitors who were not already included in

Table 1.4   Divers by Gender and Event

Event	1st pref[a]	2nd-3rd pref	N	% total	% top ten
		Females ($N = 39$)			
1M	13	6	19	83	80
3M	9	12	21	79	80
10M	17	2	19	76	80
		Males ($N = 43$)			
1M	19	9	28	79	80
3M	10	16	26	79	90
10M	14	6	20	77	80

[a]pref = event preference.

Table 1.5   Synchronized Swimmers by Event ($N = 137$)

Event	1st pref[a]	2nd-3rd pref	N	% total	% top ten
Solo	19	—	19	95	100
Duet	24	9	33	94	100
Team	94	25	119	100	100

[a]pref = event preference.

the Solo group. All other competitors were grouped into teams as a primary event. This was the first major study of synchronized swimmers at an international competition, and we were fortunate to measure more than 90% of competitors, including the top 10 finalists in each event.

Water Polo

Table 1.6 shows the breakdown of water polo competitors by gender and playing position. All participating female water polo teams were measured in KASP, and, as with synchronized swimming, this represents the first large sample of competitors measured at an international meet. The analyses in the following chapters will therefore provide landmark data for coaches and athletes in these events. A large portion of the male water polo participants was measured, which permits the comparison of data with participants at the 1968 Mexico Olympics (de Garay et al., 1974).

Table 1.6   Water Polo Players by Gender and Position

Gender	Position	N
Females	Goalkeeper	14
($N = 109$)	Center forward	27
	Center back	9
	Other[a]	59
Males	Goalkeeper	30
($N = 190$)	Center forward	40
	Center back	25
	Other[a]	95

[a]Other includes wings and utility players.

Chapter 2

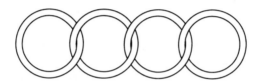

Data Management and Reports

Donald T. Drinkwater, Timothy M. Bach, Timothy R. Ackland, and Deborah A. Kerr

Any project the size and scope of KASP presents a formidable data management task. In this chapter we describe the approach taken to the process, including data entry, data inspection and correction, and individual and group report generation.

In earlier studies of this nature, raw data forms were processed by keypunch operators at remote computer sites. Increasing availability of microcomputers now makes it feasible to perform this task on-site using available personnel. This approach was used, possibly for the first time, in KASP. Therefore, we have devoted part of this chapter to the advantages and problems encountered and have suggested improvements for others who attempt to use a similar approach.

Data Entry Spreadsheet

Our intent at the major testing venues was to generate and return individual reports to athletes at the time of or shortly after the time of testing for their fuller participation in the research process. To accomplish this objective, microcomputers (IBM-PC/AT compatible) and printers were located at major testing venues.

A template was created using a commonly available spreadsheet program for IBM-PCs or compatibles. This spreadsheet was designed to provide a reasonable facsimile of the data sheet filled in at measurement stations and for ease of operation, even by inexperienced personnel. Arrow keys were used to position the cursor, and simple keystrokes activated menu functions for storing and retrieving files, printing individual data, and initializing the spreadsheet. Nondata regions of the spreadsheet were protected so that data could be entered only in legal areas. Minimal training was required to operate the program.

The use of this approach was predicated on the wide availability of such programs, which can be run on almost all IBM-compatible computers, the familiarity of many personnel with spreadsheet programs, and the ease with which such a spreadsheet template could be changed or adapted as circumstances required. Additionally, this program allowed easy collation of data from different entry stations. The approach ensured that data entry and preliminary analyses could be done using a variety of computing platforms at a variety of sites.

The spreadsheet template was partitioned into four sections: data entry, normative data comparison, data report, and data summary. A series of macro functions were written to provide menu-driven control of spreadsheet functions for data entry personnel.

Data Entry Section

Measurement data comprised one "page" of input and demographic data a second "page" in the same region of the spreadsheet. There was also a section for entry of performance results, which were added later.

Normative Data Comparison Section

To provide athletes with a meaningful report and to aid in ensuring correct data entry, we compared all measurement values to sport- and gender-specific normative values derived from similar anthropological projects. A series of centile tables were generated and stored in a separate spreadsheet file. The appropriate table was automatically entered into the master spreadsheet with input of the athlete's gender and sport. Another series of "look-up" tables contained within the spreadsheet facilitated encoding of ethnicity, gender, sport, and event.

Report Section

The report section provided athletes with feedback on their measurements and how they compared to a sport- and gender-specific normative sample. Only a single summary value was shown. Derived measurements such as somatotype and somatotype plotting coordinates were also provided. The macro function allowed the data entry personnel to print only the report section of the master template.

Data Summary Section

The fourth section of the template consisted of a single row of data containing subject identifiers, demographic and performance data, and the final values for all anthropometric dimensions, including derived values. The subject identifier was a unique sequential number based on order of measurement. A macro function transferred these data to a separate cumulative spreadsheet.

Data Entry

As mentioned, the template design of the data entry section was similar to the data sheet to minimize data entry transcription errors. As replicates for each item were entered in sequence, the program automatically calculated the mean of two measurements or determined the median of three measurements to generate a summary value. With more than three replicates, only the closest three values were entered. The summary value was used in all subsequent analyses except those pertaining to the determination of measurement reliability (see Appendix B). The spreadsheet also calculated a number of derived variables (e.g., somatotype, somatoplot coordinates, or sums of skinfolds) and generated labels from input codes for gender, ethnicity, sport, and event.

Data entry required 10 to 15 min if all measurements were recorded in triplicate and usually involved two people—one keying data and the other checking values as they were entered. If only one person entered data, he or she checked it before saving and printing.

Our original plan envisaged data entry at all measurement venues, but a shortage of personnel and time made it impossible for the mobile teams to enter data. The raw data sheets from field sites were returned to the Superdrome laboratory for data entry on the following day.

Individual Report Generation

Upon completion of data entry, the spreadsheet was used to generate a printed report. This report provided the athlete with a summary of his or her data, including derived measurements and somatotype. These values were compared on a seven-category percentile scale (0-9, 10-24, 25-44, 45-55, 56-74, 75-90, 91-100) with values of athletes from similar anthropological projects. For male and female swimmers and divers and male water polo players, comparisons were made with athletes in the same sport from anthropological projects at the Mexico City (1968) and Montreal (1976) Olympic Games. Female water polo players were compared with female swimmers from the Mexico and Montreal data. Male and female long-distance swimmers were compared with Olympic swimmers, and synchronized swimmers were compared with data collected at the 1977

Canadian Synchronized Swimming Championships. (Original data for constructing the percentile scales were provided by Carter and Ross.)

Upon completion of printing, the report was scanned by a data checker (usually a criterion anthropometrist). The data checker also plotted the athlete's somatotype on a somatochart showing the mean and distribution of somatotypes for the comparison group. After the check, the report was presented and explained to the athlete or was filed awaiting the athlete's return or delivery by one of the KASP personnel. A sample report including a somatoplot is shown in Appendixes A.2 and A.3.

Data Management

As data from the spreadsheet were saved (after initial entry of the raw data or after the data had been retrieved, corrected, and resaved) the spreadsheet updated a backup batch file containing the names of all files saved or resaved since the last backup. At the end of each day, this list was used to back up all files from the computer hard disks to floppy disks.

This daily backup list was also used to update a master list of athletes' names, sports, affiliations, and subject numbers. Such lists were not initially envisaged as a requirement of the spreadsheet. However, it became apparent early in the project that they would be useful to locate data and to plan the recruitment of subjects. This example illustrates two advantages of our approach, whereby the spreadsheet could be easily modified to accommodate changing demands and the on-site data entry provided an up-to-date and accessible data base.

At the study's completion, raw data files were retrieved and carefully compared with the original data sheets, then performance data, including overall placing and time (or score if applicable), were entered. Next, the summarized data were converted to an ASCII form and transferred to the central mainframe computing system at the University of Western Australia. Data for each individual were then sorted into one of four files (swimming, diving, water polo, or synchronized swimming) for further analysis.

Data Inspection and Correction

Data analyses were performed using SPSS-X (SPSS, Inc., 1990). Data were grouped according to gender and sport, and simple descriptive statistics were calculated. Extreme values were identified and rechecked. From these preliminary analyses, 105 instances of missing data were detected, representing 0.24% of all measurements taken.

To evaluate internal consistency of the data and to allow more sensitive error detection, multiple stepwise regression analysis was used to compare the value of each measurement with respect to a value predicted from other related measurements. Values exceeding ± 3.0 standard errors of estimate from the predicted value were then examined individually. Using this approach, 331 errors were detected. Erroneous values were checked first against the original data sheets for errors of transcription or digit reversal; 249 (0.56%) transcription errors were found and corrected. A value deemed to be in error was flagged as missing by setting it to a constant. Once this process had been completed, regression equations were recalculated and a predicted value substituted for the missing value. This occurred in 82 (0.18%) instances. Similarly, the 105 missing data values were substituted with predicted values. In all, 187 values (82 erroneous and 105 missing values), or 0.42% of all measurements, were reconstructed. After completing this checking process, we further identified errors within the data base and assigned them as missing.

Distribution

Following data correction, the four data sets were transferred from the mainframe system back to a personal computer. Together with a file containing SPSS-X control statements listing variable names and data format, the data sets (on 3.5-in floppy disks) were distributed to the authors responsible for specific analyses.

Group Analyses and Final Reports

The first analytic task was to generate group means by gender for each sport, collectively and by event. Group means were also determined for each participating team and compared with the overall sport and event means. These values were then incorporated into reports sent to the sports federations who participated in KASP. These reports were similar in format to those distributed individually to the athletes (see Appendix A.5).

Summary and Recommendations

A prerequisite for conducting this study was to be able to efficiently process data collected at different venues independent of a central computing facility. By using stand-alone computers and printers that were easily transported, measurement stations could be set up at locations convenient to the athletes, encouraging their participation.

A readily available, commonly used spreadsheet software program for personal computers facilitated the use of different IBM-compatible computers, thereby obviating the need to purchase specific equipment. Entering and analyzing data on several computers simultaneously meant a far lower risk of disrupted computing services in the event of equipment failure.

Using this simple spreadsheet program substantially facilitated data management as we set up an integrated system for data entry, executed various calculations, generated reports, and collated data. However, we did not fully achieve our objective of a very fast turnaround. Data entry, report generation, and checking required 15 to 20 min for each subject. With two data entry stations running continuously at the Superdrome site, it was not possible to keep up with the maximum throughput of the measurement stations. Peak load times required the removal of personnel from the data entry stations to assist the measurement. When the mobile teams returned from measurement sessions at hotels and residential colleges, the additional data sheets overwhelmed data entry personnel. Even under ideal conditions, athletes were seldom willing to wait for completion of their reports. To realize the objective of a report ready for the athlete following measurement would require that data recorders make direct entry at the measurement station. A system of work stations connected in a local area network would make this possible.

Use of multiple stand-alone systems created problems, because individual data files were located on a number of machines. Discovering errors after printing the data sometimes resulted in a difficult and disruptive search to find the machine on which the data was stored. Again, a local area network with a file server would eliminate this shortcoming.

The spreadsheet facilitated the detection of errors in a number of ways. Codes for sport, event, ethnicity, and sex were used to generate labels from look-up tables displayed on the data entry spreadsheet. Illegal codes generated warning error messages. Measurement and data entry error detection were facilitated by the percentile comparison table printed for each subject. The data checker could easily determine if some values were extreme. For example, a 10- to 24-percentile height and a 75- to 90-percentile bone diameter suggests that an error has been made. Unusual values of derived variables such as somatotypes also proved useful in alerting the data checker to errors. The spreadsheet could have been further enhanced as a data checking tool by incorporating a proportionality model: Each measurement could be compared with a predicted value based on height and weight measurements and flagged with any extreme measurements for the data entry personnel. The approach (Phantom Stratagem) proposed by Ross and Wilson (1974) would be extremely useful in this regard.

Overall, these procedures proved highly successful and should serve as a model for conducting similar future studies. However, to fully realize these procedural advantages, data entry should be performed directly at the measurement stations and the data entry spreadsheet should be enhanced with more sophisticated error detection algorithms. The increasing availability and ease of computer software and hardware operation make these procedures feasible for future investigatons.

Chapter 3

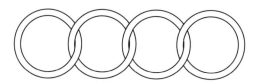

Absolute Body Size

Juan C. Mazza, Timothy R. Ackland,
Timothy M. Bach, and Patricia Cosolito

Anthropometry of sports participants has been one of the most valuable means of understanding athletic morphology at different levels of competition. Furthermore, anthropometry may elucidate the relationships between physical structure and biomechanical, physiological, and genetic profiles.

These relationships are especially important for aquatic sports, where training and performance are influenced by fluid drag and buoyancy (and consequent energy cost). Both are influenced by absolute body size parameters, as well as by relative measures like body composition. Body segment dimensions such as limb lengths, breadths, and girths also influence technique and the development of muscular power, that is, the biomechanics of swimming stroke production, somersault and twisting activities, throwing skills, and artistic movements.

As the introduction summarized, previous kinanthropometric investigations of elite aquatic athletes comprised only a few studies by Carter (1982a, 1984a), Cureton (1951), de Garay et al. (1974), and Jungmann (1976). Probably the most limiting aspect of these studies is that the small samples did not represent the multinational nature of the participant population, and they did not permit a comprehensive analytic breakdown by swimming stroke and distance, competitive events, playing position, or performance level.

This chapter describes the absolute size of competitors by sport and gender and compares the results by stroke and distance (swimming), event (diving and synchronized swimming), playing position (water polo), and performance rank (all sports).

Methods

The anthropometric dimensions selected for KASP were based on those reported in previous studies, but primarily those used at the 1976 Montreal Olympic Games (Carter, Ross, Aubry, Hebbelinck, & Borms, 1982). In addition to age, 42 absolute size dimensions were measured: body mass, stature, arm span, 8 skinfolds, 10 heights or lengths, 13 girths, and 8 breadths or depths (see Appendix A.2). Measurement techniques and equipment were based on Ross and Marfell-Jones (1991), with additional descriptions given in Appendix B for those not included in this reference.

To conserve space, this chapter uses only 34 variables for analysis. The variables, listed in tables of descriptive statistics for each sport, include age, body mass, stature, sitting height, arm span, 13 girths (head, neck, arm relaxed, arm flexed and tensed, forearm, wrist, chest, waist, hip, upper and middle thigh, calf, and ankle), 8 breadths (biacromial, transverse chest, AP chest depth, biiliocristal, humerus, wrist, hand, and femur), and 8 lengths (upper limb, arm, forearm, hand, lower limb 1, thigh 1, leg 1, and foot). For definitions of the direct and derived lengths see Appendix B. Analyses of skinfolds are included in chapters 5 and 6.

The numbers of athletes in each of the four aquatic sports are given in Tables 1.3 through 1.6 (see chapter 1). Subsequent event groupings for the various analyses within this chapter were determined as follows:

- All competitors, regardless of event or position preference, were included for descriptive statistical compilation for each sport and gender.
- Only data for competitors' first preference event or playing position were included for statistical comparison between events or positions within a sport category.
- Comparing superior performers' "best" with the others' "rest" in an event, we included data for competitors who achieved "best" status within the grouping, whether it was their primary, secondary, or tertiary event preference.

The composition of event subgroups for these analyses were chosen on the basis of similar biomechanical and physiological demands, as well as the number of subjects and their subsequent ability to meet the prerequisites for valid statistical analyses.

A series of univariate analyses of variance (ANOVA) were performed to elicit significant ($p < .05$) principal effects. With more than two groups and a significant F-ratio, the post hoc Tukey HSD procedure was applied to determine which group means differed. Due to space limitations, the analysis summary tables in this chapter include only those variables for which a significant difference was obtained. Subgroup means are ordered from low to high and presented from left to right in the post hoc analysis section of the summary tables. The groups sharing a common underline are not significantly different ($p < .05$).

When many ANOVAs are run, some could be significant by chance alone. However, the Tukey HSD procedure is very robust and conservative. The primary goal of these initial analyses was to make a preliminary identification of variables that might be performance related in each of the sports. More sophisticated analyses will be applied in future studies.

Percentile tables consisting of 31 variables were constructed for each sport and gender using all competitors in those categories. Profiles were plotted using means for competitors grouped according to their primary event only in each sport. (Blank percentile tables are available from the editors.)

Swimming

Previous Studies

Several studies have reported body size characteristics of Olympic-level swimmers (Carter et al., 1982; Cureton, 1951; de Garay et al., 1974; Jungmann, 1976; Novak et al., 1976a; and Novak, Woodward, Bestit, & Mellerowicz, 1976). Carter (1984a) provided a summary of secular trends in age, stature, and body mass variables between Olympic swimmers from the 1964 Tokyo Games through to the 1976 Montreal Games, with both male and female swimmers being progressively taller, though similar in body mass. These comparisons may be of limited value, however, given that the values for three out of four Olympics were based on self-reported rather than measured data.

Comparisons between strokes have been attempted with limited samples by de Garay et al., (1974) and Hebbelinck et al. (1975), which revealed that male freestyle (FR) swimmers were taller and had longer legs and wider hips than breaststroke (BR) and backstroke (BK) swimmers. Female swimmers did not differ on any size variable between strokes. Using data for Montreal Olympic swimmers, Carter et al. (1982) reported that of 12 size variables, a larger thigh girth for male butterfly (FL) swimmers compared to BK was the only significant difference. For females, BR were taller than FL.

Results

Descriptive statistics of age and absolute size variables for all male and female swimmers are shown in Table 3.1

Comparison Between Strokes

Table 3.2 summarizes the results of univariate analyses of variance and Tukey's post hoc tests for significant size differences between competitors in the various

Table 3.1   Descriptive Statistics for Male and Female Swimmers

Variable	Unit	Male swimmers ($n = 231$)		Female swimmers ($n = 170$)	
		M	SD	M	SD
Age	yr	21.3	2.7	19.6	2.9
Body mass	kg	78.4	7.1	63.1	5.9
Stature	cm	183.8	7.1	171.5	7.0
Sitting height	cm	96.5	3.5	90.7	3.4
Arm span	cm	192.5	7.8	176.3	7.8
Girths	cm				
Head		57.1	1.5	54.8	1.5
Neck		38.8	1.6	33.5	1.3
Arm relaxed		32.0	1.7	28.8	1.7
Arm flexed		34.5	1.8	30.1	1.7
Forearm		28.2	1.3	24.7	1.0
Wrist		17.1	0.8	15.4	0.7
Chest		103.2	4.4	92.0	4.0
Waist		79.4	3.5	69.4	3.7
Hip		94.8	3.6	93.1	3.8
Upper thigh		56.1	2.6	54.9	2.7
Middle thigh		53.2	2.5	50.6	2.4
Calf		37.6	1.8	34.9	1.7
Ankle		22.6	1.1	21.1	1.7
Breadths	cm				
Biacromial		42.5	1.9	38.5	1.8
Transverse chest		30.7	1.7	27.5	1.6
AP chest		21.2	1.6	18.8	1.5
Biiliocristal		28.5	1.5	27.8	1.6
Humerus		7.4	0.4	6.4	0.4
Wrist		5.9	0.4	5.3	0.3
Hand		8.6	0.5	7.7	0.4
Femur		9.9	0.5	9.1	0.5
Lengths	cm				
Upper limb		84.6	4.6	78.1	5.0
Arm		36.2	1.9	33.4	1.9
Forearm		27.5	1.4	25.1	1.4
Hand		20.8	1.0	19.3	1.0
Lower limb 1		87.2	4.7	80.8	4.8
Thigh 1		38.1	2.7	35.6	2.6
Leg 1		49.1	2.9	45.2	2.7
Foot		27.4	1.4	24.9	1.3

Table 3.2   ANOVA Summary of Significant Size Differences for Swimmers by Stroke

Variable		Post hoc Tukey HSD				F^a	p
Males							
Stature	181.6 BR	181.8 FL	183.3 IM	185.7 FR	188.6 BK	4.20	.003
Head girth	56.4 BR	56.6 FL	57.3 BK	57.4 FR	57.5 IM	3.81	.005
Transverse chest B	30.1 BR	30.2 IM	30.5 FL	30.7 BK	31.1 FR	2.92	.020
Lower limb 1 length	85.7 FL	85.9 BR	86.3 IM	88.4 BK	88.4 FR	4.01	.004
Thigh 1 length	37.2 FL	37.4 BR	37.8 IM	38.6 BK	38.6 FR	2.92	.020
Females							
Body mass	61.2 BR	61.7 FL	62.8 IM	63.1 BK	65.0 FR	2.60	.040
Neck girth	32.9 BR	33.1 BK	33.3 FL	33.5 IM	33.9 FR	4.25	.003
Transverse chest	26.6 BR	27.4 BK	27.6 FL	27.6 IM	27.8 FR	3.27	.010
Forearm length	24.5 FL	24.9 BR	24.9 IM	25.5 BK	25.7 FR	4.77	.001
Lower limb 1 length	79.2 FL	80.0 BR	80.0 IM	81.6 BK	82.7 FR	3.58	.010
Thigh 1 length	34.8 FL	35.1 BR	35.1 IM	35.7 BK	36.7 FR	3.69	.070
Arm span	173.9 FL	174.2 BR	176.3 IM	178.5 BK	178.9 FR	3.43	.010

Note. Body mass in kilograms, all other variables in centimeters. All stroke groups include 50 m, 100 m, and 200 m, competitors except IM which includes 200 + 400 m competitors. Sample sizes for males: BR = 37, FL = 41, IM = 21, FR = 71, BK = 28; for females: BR = 28, FL = 29, IM = 21, BK = 18, FR = 52. ^{a}F = F-ratio.

strokes. For the purposes of this analysis, FR competitors, whose primary distance was 400 m or greater, were excluded. Only five absolute size measures for males and seven for females were different between strokes. Male FR were taller than BR and FL and possessed greater head girth and transverse chest breadth than BR. This size difference is also apparent for the lower limb dimensions, where FR have longer lower limbs compared to FL and BR and longer thighs than FL.

Female FR are heavier than BR and possess greater neck girth and transverse chest breadth. With respect to the upper limb, FR possess longer forearms than FL and greater arm span compared to FL and BR. In the lower limb, FR similarly had a greater lower limb length than FL and longer thighs than FL and BR. These differences, as noted between competitors within the various strokes, may be due to self-selection characteristics that are advantageous for performance in that stroke.

FR are generally taller than BR and FL, and this difference appears due to greater lower limb dimensions rather than trunk length. Substantial differences in lower limb actions between freestyle and breaststroke mechanics may be associated with these differences.

Comparison Between Distances

In this section a comparison of freestyle events only was made, because the variation in distance for the other strokes was small. Freestyle events were grouped as short distance (SD = 50 + 100 m), middle distance (MD = 200 + 400 m), middle to long distance (ML = 800 m for females or 1500 m for males), or long distance (LD = 25 km). Differences are shown on 11 dimensions between various distance groups for male swimmers in Table 3.3 and Figure 3.1.

With respect to lengths, LD were smaller than SD in stature and sitting height, hand and foot lengths, and arm span. For girth measures, however, the ML group demonstrated most differences with other groups, having smaller neck and upper thigh girths compared to SD, MD, and LD. In addition, ML had smaller flexed arm girth compared to SD, and smaller middle thigh girths than SD or LD. This suggests ML possess less muscularity than swimmers of other distances. LD had the greatest anteroposterior (AP) chest depth, yet with a significantly narrower biacromial breadth than SD.

Differences are shown for 16 dimensions between various distance groups for female swimmers in Table 3.4 and Figure 3.2. As with the male competitors, the female LD were significantly smaller in many linear dimensions compared to SD and MD. These dimensions include standing and sitting height; upper limb, arm, and hand lengths; lower limb 1; thigh 1; leg 1; foot lengths; and arm span. Clearly, the LD swimmer is smaller in absolute dimensions. Proportionality differences are explored further in chapter 5. Female SD and MD also possess greater biacromial, wrist, and hand breadths compared to LD.

Best Versus Rest

Here we compare swimmers who were ranked in the top 12 placings, that is, those who swam in Final A plus the first four placings in Final B (Best group),

Table 3.3   ANOVA Summary of Significant Size Differences for Male Swimmers by Distance

Variable	Post hoc Tukey HSD				F	p
Stature	179.6 LD	183.1 ML	185.2 MD	186.4 SD	3.10	.030
Neck girth	37.5 ML	39.0 MD	39.0 SD	39.4 LD	3.45	.020
Flexed arm girth	32.9 ML	34.3 LD	34.5 MD	35.0 SD	3.53	.020
Upper thigh girth	54.9 ML	55.7 SD	55.7 LD	56.1 MD	4.56	.005
Middle thigh girth	50.6 ML	52.9 MD	52.9 SD	53.8 LD	3.37	.020
Biacromial breadth	41.1 LD	41.8 ML	42.6 MD	42.7 SD	3.12	.030
AP chest depth	20.3 ML	21.1 SD	21.3 MD	22.2 LD	3.12	.030
Hand length	20.2 LD	20.6 MD	20.8 ML	21.1 SD	3.67	.010
Foot length	26.3 LD	27.3 MD	27.3 ML	27.6 SD	3.22	.020
Sitting height	94.1 LD	95.6 ML	96.6 MD	97.6 SD	4.11	.010
Arm span	186.6 LD	193.2 ML	193.4 MD	195.2 SD	4.24	.010

Note. SD = 50 + 100 m FR (n = 47), MD = 200 + 400 m FR (n = 34), ML = 1500 m FR (n = 10), LD = long-distance swimmers, 25 km (n = 13).

to swimmers who were placed outside of the top 12 (Rest group). Separate analyses for the freestyle events were performed for FR 50 + 100 m, FR 200 + 400 m and FR 800 m or 1500 m; the 50 + 100 + 200 m events were grouped for BR, BK, and FL analyses. Both 200 m and 400 m individual medley (IM) swimmers were grouped together for this analysis. Table 3.5 provides a summary of significant size differences for Best versus Rest in FR 50 + 100 m. The better male swimmers were older and taller and possessed longer upper and lower limb segments; whereas females in the Best group demonstrated greater lower limb

PERCENTILE	Age	Body mass	Height	Sum of 6 skinfolds	Head girth	Relaxed arm girth	Flexed arm girth	Forearm girth	Wrist girth	Chest girth	Waist girth	Hip girth	Upper thigh girth	Calf girth	Ankle girth
P95	26.0	88.6	195.4	73.3	59.7	34.9	37.7	30.2	18.5	110.1	85.8	100.6	60.1	40.6	24.6
P90	25.2	87.0	192.7	63.1	58.9	34.4	37.0	29.8	18.1	108.9	84.2	99.8	59.6	40.1	24.2
P80	23.8	84.8	189.6	54.8	58.3	33.6	36.1	29.3	17.8	107.0	82.1	97.6	58.4	39.2	23.6
P70	22.6	82.7	187.3	51.1	57.8	32.9	35.5	28.9	17.5	105.6	81.0	96.4	57.4	38.4	23.1
P60	21.7	80.8	185.9	48.1	57.5	32.5	35.1	28.6	17.3	104.5	80.3	95.5	56.7	37.9	22.8
P50	21.1	78.7	184.3	45.6	57.1	32.1	34.5	28.2	17.1	103.5	79.3	94.8	56.2	37.5	22.5
P40	20.5	76.5	182.0	42.6	56.7	31.6	34.1	27.9	16.9	102.4	78.4	93.8	55.6	37.1	22.2
P30	19.8	75.0	180.0	40.0	56.2	31.1	33.6	27.5	16.6	101.2	77.8	92.9	54.9	36.6	21.9
P20	19.0	72.1	177.5	37.0	55.7	30.5	33.0	27.1	16.4	99.6	76.5	91.9	53.8	36.1	21.5
P10	17.7	68.5	174.2	34.9	55.2	29.9	32.2	26.5	16.1	96.8	75.0	90.0	52.7	35.3	21.2
P05	17.0	66.6	171.9	33.1	54.7	29.4	31.5	26.2	15.9	95.6	73.4	89.0	52.1	34.8	20.8
M	21.3	78.4	183.7	60.6	57.1	32.0	34.5	28.2	17.1	103.2	79.4	94.8	56.1	37.6	22.6
SD	2.7	7.1	7.1	15.5	1.5	1.7	1.8	1.3	0.8	4.4	3.5	3.6	2.6	1.8	1.1

● - - - 50 & 100 FR   ▲ - - - ▲ 200 & 400 FR   ○——— 1500 FR   □ LDS

Figure 3.1   Mean body-size profiles for male freestyle swimmers by event distance. Plotted on percentiles derived from all male swimmers, *(continued)*

n = 231

	P95	P90	P80	P70	P60	P50	P40	P30	P20	P10	P05	M	SD
Arm span	205.6	202.0	199.2	196.6	195.0	192.5	190.5	188.2	186.3	182.6	179.0	192.5	7.8
Sitting height	101.9	100.9	99.4	98.2	96.6	97.0	96.3	93.2	93.3	91.4	90.4	96.5	3.5
Foot length	29.9	29.3	28.5	28.0	27.6	27.3	27.0	26.6	26.3	25.6	25.3	27.4	1.4
Leg length	54.0	52.7	51.0	50.5	50.0	49.3	48.6	47.9	46.6	45.6	44.8	49.1	2.9
Thigh length	50.4	49.7	48.5	47.5	46.8	45.8	45.4	44.9	43.9	42.7	41.7	46.1	2.8
Lower limb length	110.2	108.3	106.5	104.7	103.2	102.3	100.5	99.3	97.0	95.3	93.1	95.3	4.9
Hand length	22.4	22.1	21.7	21.3	21.0	20.7	20.5	20.3	20.0	19.5	19.2	20.8	1.0
Upper limb length	91.4	89.1	87.4	86.4	85.5	84.2	83.4	82.6	81.6	79.8	78.0	84.6	4.6
Femur breadth	10.8	10.5	10.3	10.2	10.1	10.0	9.8	9.7	9.6	9.3	9.2	9.9	0.5
Hand breadth	9.4	9.3	9.0	8.9	8.8	8.7	8.6	8.5	8.3	8.0	7.9	8.6	0.5
Humerus breadth	8.0	7.8	7.7	7.6	7.5	7.4	7.3	7.2	7.0	6.8	6.7	7.4	0.4
Billiocristal breadth	31.1	30.5	29.8	29.1	28.8	28.4	28.1	27.8	27.4	26.5	26.1	28.5	1.5
AP chest breadth	23.8	23.5	22.5	22.0	21.5	21.2	20.8	20.6	20.0	19.3	18.7	21.2	1.6
Transverse chest breadth	33.6	32.8	32.0	31.5	31.2	30.8	30.4	29.8	29.3	28.2	27.7	30.7	1.7
Biacromial breadth	45.7	44.9	44.1	43.5	42.9	42.5	42.0	41.5	41.0	40.3	39.8	42.5	39.7

Figure 3.1 (continued)

Table 3.4   ANOVA Summary of Significant Size Differences for Female Swimmers by Distance

Variable	Post hoc Tukey HSD				F	p
Age	18.4 MD	19.3 ML	20.9 SD	22.8 LD	6.31	.001
Stature	162.6 LD	171.9 ML	173.9 SD	174.0 MD	8.52	.000
Head girth	53.8 LD	54.8 SD	55.0 ML	55.4 MD	2.80	.040
Biacromial breadth	37.0 LD	38.6 ML	38.9 MD	38.9 SD	3.55	.020
Wrist breadth	5.1 LD	5.1 ML	5.3 MD	5.3 SD	4.32	.010
Hand breadth	7.2 LD	7.7 ML	7.8 SD	7.9 MD	4.93	.004
Upper limb length	74.7 LD	78.4 MD	79.0 SD	79.3 ML	4.99	.003
Arm length	32.1 LD	33.7 ML	33.8 SD	34.1 MD	3.12	.030
Hand length	18.4 LD	19.0 ML	19.4 SD	19.5 MD	3.80	.010
Lower limb 1 length	75.9 LD	80.9 ML	82.7 MD	82.9 SD	6.39	.001
Thigh 1 length	33.1 LD	35.9 ML	36.4 MD	37.0 SD	5.94	.010
Leg 1 length	42.9 LD	44.9 ML	45.9 SD	46.3 MD	4.88	.004
Foot length	23.4 LD	25.0 SD	25.3 MD	26.7 ML	7.05	.001
Sitting height	86.7 LD	91.0 SD	91.1 ML	91.3 MD	5.17	.003
Arm span	167.7 LD	177.3 ML	178.9 SD	179.6 MD	7.61	.001

Note. Age in years, all other variables in centimeters. SD = 50 + 100 m FR ($n = 31$), MD = 200 + 400 m FR ($n = 27$), ML = 800 m FR ($n = 6$), LD = long-distance swimmers, 25 km ($n = 10$).

PERCENTILE	Age	Body mass	Height	Sum of 6 skinfolds	Head girth	Relaxed arm girth	Flexed arm girth	Forearm girth	Wrist girth	Chest girth	Waist girth	Hip girth	Upper thigh girth	Calf girth	Ankle girth
P95	25.2	73.1	183.8	110.4	57.0	31.8	33.0	26.5	16.5	99.5	75.6	98.5	59.6	37.9	23.0
P90	22.6	70.8	181.1	93.8	56.7	30.8	32.2	26.1	16.3	96.9	74.2	97.5	58.2	37.0	22.6
P80	21.3	68.5	178.1	87.4	56.1	30.2	31.5	25.6	16.0	94.7	72.5	96.4	57.1	36.3	22.1
P70	20.6	66.3	175.4	81.5	55.6	29.9	31.0	25.3	15.8	93.7	71.1	95.5	56.4	35.9	21.7
P60	19.9	64.1	172.8	76.6	55.3	29.2	30.5	24.9	15.5	93.1	70.1	94.3	55.8	35.3	21.4
P50	19.2	62.7	171.0	70.2	54.8	28.8	30.1	24.7	15.4	92.0	69.3	93.2	55.1	34.9	21.2
P40	18.5	61.2	170.0	64.4	54.5	28.3	29.6	24.5	15.2	91.0	68.5	92.0	54.3	34.5	20.8
P30	17.9	60.1	168.0	59.8	54.0	27.9	29.2	24.2	15.0	89.9	67.5	91.2	53.5	34.0	20.5
P20	17.2	58.8	165.5	55.2	53.5	27.4	28.7	23.9	14.8	88.6	66.4	90.3	52.6	33.5	20.1
P10	16.2	55.4	160.9	50.8	52.7	26.7	28.1	23.5	14.5	87.3	64.7	88.1	51.5	32.9	19.6
P05	15.3	52.9	159.3	46.3	52.2	26.1	27.4	23.0	14.2	84.9	64.0	85.9	50.5	32.5	19.2
M	19.6	63.1	171.5	88.9	54.8	28.8	30.1	24.7	15.4	92.0	69.4	93.1	54.9	34.9	21.1
SD	2.9	5.9	7.0	24.7	1.5	1.7	1.7	1.0	0.7	4.0	3.7	3.8	2.7	1.7	1.2

● - - ● 50 + 100 FR   ▲ - - ▲ 200 + 400 FR   ○——○ 800 FR   □ LDS

(continued)

Figure 3.2 Mean body-size profiles for female freestyle swimmers by event distance. Plotted on percentiles derived from all female swimmers, $n = 170$.

PERCENTILE	Arm span	Sitting height	Foot length	Leg length	Thigh length	Lower limb length	Hand length	Upper limb length	Femur breadth	Hand breadth	Humerus breadth	Biiliocristal breadth	AP chest breadth	Transverse chest breadth	Biacromial breadth
P95	188.9	96.5	27.1	49.6	47.9	102.6	21.0	84.3	9.8	8.4	7.1	30.5	21.3	30.1	41.4
P90	186.8	94.8	26.4	48.5	47.1	100.9	20.4	83.0	9.8	8.2	6.9	30.1	21.0	29.3	41.0
P80	183.9	93.2	25.9	47.3	45.9	98.9	20.0	80.7	9.5	8.1	6.7	29.0	20.1	28.9	40.2
P70	180.4	92.5	25.5	46.6	45.4	96.9	19.7	79.8	9.3	8.0	6.6	28.6	19.6	28.4	39.5
P60	178.6	91.7	25.2	46.2	44.8	95.6	19.5	77.8	9.2	7.9	6.5	28.2	19.2	28.0	39.1
P50	176.6	90.6	25.0	45.4	44.2	94.3	19.2	77.6	9.1	7.8	6.4	27.8	18.7	27.3	38.4
P40	174.4	90.1	24.7	44.4	43.4	92.8	19.0	76.5	9.0	7.6	6.3	27.5	18.5	27.0	38.0
P30	171.6	89.3	24.4	43.9	42.4	91.0	18.7	75.9	8.9	7.6	6.2	27.2	18.0	26.6	37.3
P20	170.0	87.7	23.8	42.9	41.6	89.2	18.5	75.1	8.7	7.4	6.1	26.5	17.5	26.3	36.8
P10	165.9	86.0	23.2	41.3	40.2	87.2	18.0	73.0	8.5	7.2	5.9	25.5	17.0	25.5	36.2
P05	162.2	85.3	22.5	40.6	39.4	86.1	17.7	71.8	8.4	7.0	5.7	24.9	16.5	24.8	35.5
M	176.3	90.7	24.9	45.2	43.8	89.0	19.3	78.1	9.1	7.7	6.4	27.8	18.8	27.5	38.5
SD	7.8	3.4	1.3	2.7	2.6	4.9	1.0	5.0	0.5	0.4	0.4	1.6	1.5	1.6	1.8

Figure 3.2 (continued)

Table 3.5   ANOVA Summary of Significant Size Differences for 50 + 100 m Freestyle Swimmers by Performance Rank: Best Group (Males *n* = 18, Females *n* = 17); Rest Group (Males *n* = 40, Females *n* = 29)

Variable	Best M	SD	Rest M	SD	F	p
Males						
Age	22.8	2.6	21.1	2.8	4.44	.040
Stature	188.9	7.9	184.3	6.6	5.36	.020
Biiliocristal breadth	29.3	1.7	28.3	1.4	5.33	.020
Humerus breadth	7.6	0.3	7.4	0.4	6.35	.010
Upper limb length	87.2	4.3	84.6	3.7	5.54	.020
Arm length	37.6	2.1	35.9	1.8	8.95	.005
Lower limb 1 length	91.1	5.6	87.3	4.1	8.57	.005
Leg 1 length	51.4	3.5	49.3	2.9	5.68	.020
Females						
Biiliocristal breadth	29.0	1.6	27.4	1.5	12.61	.001
Wrist breadth	5.4	0.2	5.2	0.3	5.91	.020
Leg 1 length	46.7	2.2	45.1	2.5	4.54	.040
Foot length	25.5	0.8	24.7	1.1	6.87	.010

Note. Age in years, all other variables in centimeters.

lengths and greater biiliocristal and wrist breadths compared to those in the Rest group.

Although differences in skeletal dimensions distinguish Best and Rest performers in FR 200 + 400 m, several girth measurements provided a significant discrimination between Best and Rest male MD FR (Table 3.6). Best performers were older, heavier, and taller than the Rest, with greater upper limb, chest, and thigh girths and greater upper and lower limb segmental lengths. For females, the better performers were significantly taller, with broader shoulders and chests, and possessed greater upper and lower limb segment lengths.

In stark contrast to the short- and middle-distance events, very few measures separated Best FR 1500 m (male) and FR 800 m (female) performers from the Rest group. Age once again distinguished Best and Rest for FR 1500 m, with the Best group being older. Better performers also had larger humerus and hand breadths. The groups did not differ in stature, but a greater sitting height for FR 1500 m and FR 800 m was shown to be advantageous. No Best versus Rest analyses were performed for LD due to the small sample of swimmers in this group.

Table 3.7 contains a summary of significant size differences for BR. For the male BR the Best performers were clearly taller and heavier; concomitant differences were seen in eight girths, four breadths, and eight upper and lower

Table 3.6   ANOVA Summary of Significant Size Differences for 200 + 400 m Free-style Swimmers by Performance Rank: Best Group (Males *n* = 17, Females *n* = 20); Rest Group (Males *n* = 23, Females *n* = 39)

Variable	Best M	SD	Rest M	SD	F	p
Males						
Age	22.0	2.2	20.2	2.9	5.39	.020
Body mass	83.0	5.7	76.7	7.6	9.30	.005
Stature	188.7	5.3	183.6	8.0	5.68	.020
Arm relaxed girth	33.1	1.9	31.6	1.6	9.49	.005
Arm flexed girth	35.5	1.7	34.0	1.7	8.40	.005
Forearm girth	28.9	1.1	27.9	1.1	8.82	.005
Chest girth	106.1	3.4	102.4	4.8	7.92	.005
Middle thigh girth	53.7	1.7	51.9	2.8	5.97	.020
Transverse chest breadth	31.9	1.8	30.4	1.8	7.84	.005
Upper limb length	89.1	9.1	84.7	4.4	5.94	.020
Lower limb 1 length	90.9	3.7	87.2	5.6	6.22	.010
Leg 1 length	51.3	3.3	49.1	3.2	5.29	.020
Foot length	28.1	1.1	27.2	1.5	4.44	.040
Females						
Height	176.1	4.7	171.4	6.8	6.75	.010
Biacromial breadth	39.7	1.2	38.2	1.7	10.56	.001
Transverse chest breadth	28.3	1.3	27.1	1.7	6.77	.010
Upper limb length	80.6	3.4	77.9	3.2	6.93	.010
Arm length	34.9	1.6	33.5	2.0	6.20	.020
Forearm length	26.1	1.4	25.1	1.0	6.77	.010
Lower limb 1 length	84.0	4.3	81.0	5.3	4.21	.047
Thigh 1 length	37.3	2.2	35.4	2.8	5.84	.020
Arm span	182.4	6.4	177.2	7.9	5.54	.020

Note. Age in years, body mass in kilograms, all other variables in centimeters.

limb segment lengths compared to those in the Rest group. It would seem then that a muscular physique and its implication for power development are discriminating factors in male BR performance. No stature or body mass differences were noted for the better female BR, but they possessed greater hand and wrist breadths, as well as longer upper limb and foot dimensions, compared to the Rest.

Segmental lengths dominate the differences between Best and Rest BK for both male and female swimmers (Table 3.8). The better male swimmers were significantly older and taller than the Rest, with longer upper and lower limb segment dimensions. For the better female swimmers, only upper limb, forearm, and foot length were significantly greater.

Table 3.7   ANOVA Summary of Significant Size Differences for 50 + 100 + 200 m Breaststroke Swimmers by Performance Rank: Best Group (Males *n* = 21, Females *n* = 19); Rest Group (Males *n* = 18, Females *n* = 9)

Variable	Best M	Best SD	Rest M	Rest SD	F	p
Males						
Body mass	79.2	6.5	72.8	5.2	11.26	.002
Stature	183.5	5.4	178.5	5.9	7.82	.008
Neck girth	39.1	1.6	37.9	1.5	5.61	.020
Arm flexed girth	35.1	2.1	33.8	1.1	5.51	.020
Forearm girth	28.6	1.4	27.5	1.1	7.14	.010
Wrist girth	17.5	0.6	16.6	0.7	14.27	.001
Chest girth	103.8	4.6	100.2	3.8	6.72	.010
Upper thigh girth	56.9	2.3	55.4	1.9	5.14	.030
Middle thigh girth	54.5	2.4	52.4	1.7	9.95	.003
Ankle girth	22.9	1.0	22.0	1.3	6.27	.020
AP chest depth	22.2	1.5	20.4	1.4	15.19	.001
Humerus breadth	7.5	0.4	7.1	0.6	9.09	.005
Wrist breadth	6.0	0.2	5.6	0.5	8.04	.007
Hand breadth	8.9	0.4	8.4	0.6	10.92	.002
Upper limb length	84.7	3.8	81.7	2.9	7.21	.010
Arm length	36.0	1.9	34.7	1.9	4.28	.040
Forearm length	27.5	1.4	26.6	0.9	5.74	.020
Hand length	21.2	1.1	20.4	0.9	5.97	.020
Lower limb 1 length	86.9	3.4	83.9	3.9	6.61	.010
Leg 1 length	49.4	2.2	47.2	1.7	11.24	.002
Foot length	28.1	1.7	26.9	1.0	6.34	.020
Arm span	192.8	6.2	186.8	5.5	10.24	.000
Females						
Wrist breadth	5.4	0.3	5.0	0.4	6.18	.020
Hand breadth	7.9	0.4	7.5	0.4	8.78	.006
Arm length	33.4	1.9	31.6	1.3	5.87	.020
Foot length	25.5	1.2	24.3	0.6	8.55	.007
Arm span	176.4	8.7	169.4	5.4	4.82	.040

Note. Body mass in kilograms, all other variables in centimeters.

Table 3.9 presents Best versus Rest comparisons for FL. Few absolute size measures separate male competitors except those for age, stature, waist girth, and sitting height, with the Best swimmers being older and possessing larger

Table 3.8   ANOVA Summary of Significant Size Differences 50 + 100 + 200 m Backstroke Swimmers by Performance Rank: Best Group (Males *n* = 17, Females *n* = 14); Rest Group (Males *n* = 20, Females *n* = 11)

	Best		Rest			
Variable	M	SD	M	SD	F	p
Males						
Age	22.3	2.4	19.8	3.0	7.66	.009
Stature	188.1	6.3	182.8	6.5	6.30	.020
Wrist breadth	6.0	0.3	5.7	0.4	5.94	.020
Upper limb length	86.2	3.9	83.7	2.9	4.92	.030
Arm length	37.1	1.9	35.9	1.6	4.45	.040
Hand length	21.3	1.2	20.5	0.8	5.60	.020
Lower limb 1 length	89.7	4.2	86.3	3.9	6.33	.020
Leg 1 length	50.5	2.1	48.7	2.2	6.31	.020
Foot length	28.2	1.6	27.1	1.1	5.58	.020
Arm span	196.6	8.0	191.5	6.8	4.44	.040
Females						
Upper limb length	79.9	3.1	77.1	2.7	5.36	.030
Forearm length	25.8	1.1	24.9	0.8	5.55	.030
Foot length	25.3	1.1	24.1	1.1	7.27	.010

Note. Age in years, all other variables in centimeters.

dimensions. Better female FL, however, had broader upper bodies with greater biacromial, transverse chest, biiliocristal, wrist, and hand breadths than the Rest. The better performers were also taller and had longer feet. The combined effect of these differences in the limb dimensions may provide a hydrodynamic advantage for the development of propulsion through the arm pull and leg kick in this event.

The IM event requires that swimmers be proficient in all four strokes, but typically competitors are particularly strong in one or two of the component strokes. Morphological differences are therefore less likely between Best and Rest than in the specialist events. Few differences were indeed noted between Best and Rest male and female IM (Table 3.10). The better male IM possessed greater lower limb segment lengths, arm length, and biiliocristal breadth compared with the Rest. For females, only waist and ankle girth plus transverse chest breadth were greater for Best IM compared to the Rest.

Discussion

A unique aspect of the KASP data is the ability to compare the morphology of swimmers. Several size differences were noted between swimmers in various

Table 3.9   ANOVA Summary of Significant Size Differences for 50 + 100 + 200 m Butterfly Swimmers by Performance Rank: Best Group (Male *n* = 22, Females *n* = 21); Rest Group (Males *n* = 29, Female, *n* = 19)

Variable	Best		Rest			
	M	SD	*M*	SD	F	*p*
Males						
Age	22.3	2.7	20.0	2.2	11.62	.010
Stature	184.5	6.0	180.0	6.4	6.62	.010
Waist girth	81.0	3.9	78.6	2.8	6.39	.010
Sitting height	97.7	3.2	94.9	2.9	10.31	.002
Females						
Stature	171.9	5.4	168.3	4.8	4.69	.040
Wrist girth	15.4	0.4	15.0	0.7	4.84	.030
Biacromial breadth	39.4	1.6	38.2	1.6	6.72	.010
Transverse chest breadth	27.9	1.1	26.9	1.8	5.16	.030
Biiliocristal breadth	28.1	1.3	27.0	1.9	4.33	.040
Wrist breadth	5.4	0.2	5.1	0.2	15.22	.001
Hand breadth	7.9	0.2	7.6	0.4	10.40	.003
Foot length	25.1	0.9	24.3	0.9	7.67	.009

Note. Age in years, all other variables in centimeters.

strokes. For example, FR are taller, with longer lower limbs and broader chests, than FL and BR. Furthermore, female FR possess longer upper limbs than BR. The arm pull pattern for BR does not require particularly long limbs because a wide hand path is not always the optimal pattern for generating effective force and may disrupt stroke timing (Maglischo, 1982). A long pull path afforded by long body semgents, however, would be advantageous for FR (particularly for SD and MD events) and for BK. Provided the swimmer has sufficient muscular power to complement the longer segments, greater propulsive force may be developed for each FR stroke with the longer levers.

The differences noted between FR at varying distances may be related to differences in requirements for power production and energy expenditure. SD and MD generally have larger upper limbs and broader shoulders and are therefore suited for high power output. ML display smaller girths at a number of sites, which suggest a less muscular physique and may improve swimming economy through decreased limb segment motions. LD, however, have decreased frontal resistance (narrow biacromial breadth) and decreased surface area (as a result of smaller stature and body mass). Smaller surface area may be effective in reducing heat loss as well as hydrodynamic drag, which may be a factor influencing success over these extreme distances.

Table 3.10   ANOVA Summary of Significant Size Differences for 200 + 400 m Individual Medley Swimmers by Performance Rank: Best Group (Males n = 12, Female n = 16); Rest Group (Males n = 23, Females n = 15)

Variable	Best M	Best SD	Rest M	Rest SD	F	p
Males						
Biiliocristal breadth	29.3	1.8	28.1	1.2	5.32	.03
Arm length	37.3	1.7	35.8	1.6	6.88	.01
Lower limb 1 length	89.8	3.7	85.7	4.7	6.85	.01
Thigh 1 length	39.4	2.4	37.4	2.1	6.64	.02
Leg 1 length	50.4	3.0	48.3	2.8	4.20	.05
Females						
Waist girth	70.81	3.63	68.4	2.9	4.23	.05
Ankle girth	21.07	0.95	20.3	1.0	4.57	.04
Transverse chest breadth	28.05	1.63	26.7	1.2	6.37	.02

Note. All variables in centimeters.

In distinguishing between Best and Rest, a general pattern emerges in favor of older and taller athletes with larger limb, hand, and foot lengths. Age could also be a factor because of associated physiological and structural maturity, but emotional and psychological maturity are likely to be important factors.

Diving

Previous Studies

Anthropometry of elite divers has been reported in Carter (1982a, 1984a), de Garay et al. (1974), Hebbelinck et al. (1975), and Rodriguez et al. (1986). Based on data reported by delegations, female divers (n = 26) at the 1976 Montreal Olympic Games were smaller (M = 163.2 cm) and lighter (M = 53.0 kg) than swimmers. Similarly, the male divers (n = 28) were smaller in stature (M = 171.5 cm) and lighter (M = 66.0 kg) than swimmers and water polo players (Carter, 1984a). De Garay et al. (1974) showed a similar trend for aquatic athletes from the 1968 Mexico Olympic Games, with divers displaying stature and body mass characteristics more closely aligned with gymnasts than with swimmers or water polo players. No attempt to assess possible differences between springboard and platform diving specialists has been reported.

Results

Descriptive statistics of age and absolute size variables for all female and male divers are shown in Table 3.11.

Table 3.11   Descriptive Statistics for Female and Male Divers

Variable	Units	Female divers (n = 39) M	SD	Male divers (n = 43) M	SD
Age	yr	20.9	3.8	22.2	4.6
Body mass	kg	53.7	5.5	66.7	10.2
Stature	cm	161.2	6.0	170.9	8.6
Sitting height	cm	86.3	3.4	90.3	4.3
Arm span	cm	164.4	6.5	177.7	8.9
Girths	cm				
Head		53.8	1.6	56.0	1.9
Neck		32.5	1.3	37.8	2.2
Arm relaxed		26.9	1.7	30.6	2.8
Arm flexed		28.0	1.7	32.5	3.0
Forearm		23.4	1.1	27.2	2.1
Wrist		14.8	0.7	16.6	1.0
Chest		85.0	4.3	95.2	7.3
Waist		65.6	2.5	74.5	5.1
Hip		87.0	4.8	89.5	5.8
Upper thigh		52.3	3.5	53.7	4.2
Middle thigh		48.7	3.2	51.3	3.8
Calf		33.9	2.0	36.4	2.5
Ankle		20.3	1.0	21.6	1.3
Breadths	cm				
Biacromial		36.5	1.6	39.7	2.4
Transverse chest		25.8	1.3	28.8	2.4
AP chest		17.2	1.4	19.1	1.7
Biiliocristal		26.0	1.7	26.7	1.6
Humerus		5.9	0.5	6.8	0.6
Wrist		4.9	0.6	5.6	0.5
Hand		7.3	0.6	8.1	0.6
Femur		8.4	0.6	9.3	0.6
Lengths	cm				
Upper limb		72.3	3.0	77.9	4.1
Arm		31.0	1.7	33.1	2.0
Forearm		23.1	1.1	25.4	1.6
Hand		18.2	0.8	19.4	1.0
Lower limb 1		74.9	3.8	80.7	5.2
Thigh 1		32.4	2.1	34.8	2.7
Leg 1		42.5	2.0	45.9	2.8
Foot		23.2	1.0	25.5	1.5

Comparison Between Events

Mean values of absolute size variables for female divers who competed in 1 m (1M) ($n = 13$), 3 m (3M) ($n = 9$), or 10 m (10M) ($n = 17$) primary events are presented in Figure 3.3. Few dimensions distinguished performers in these events; however, upper thigh girth and transverse chest breadth were smaller for 10M performers compared to 1M performers. In contrast, no significant differences in absolute dimensions were recorded for male divers, the mean values for whom appear in Figure 3.4.

Best Versus Rest

In this section a comparison is made between divers who were ranked in the top 10 placings (Best group) for performance in any primary, secondary, or tertiary event preference and those competitors who did not achieve top 10 status (Rest group). The analysis showed female divers competing at the World Champion-ships (Best $n = 21$, Rest $n = 19$) to be homogeneous in absolute size. Smaller values for head girth (F = 10.59, $p < .01$) and forearm length (F = 9.43, $p < .01$) provided the only differences between Best and Rest. Similarly with males, the Best divers ($n = 19$) had smaller head girth than the Rest ($n = 24$) (F = 4.18, $p < .05$). No other differences were noted for male divers.

Discussion

Both female and male divers who competed at the 1991 World Championships in Perth were shown to be morphologically homogeneous in same-gender categories. Few differences in size were shown for Best versus Rest performers; a less massive physique (suggested by smaller AP chest depths and upper thigh girths for female 10M compared to 1M) were the only measures that distinguished competitors between events. Confirmation of this trend is supported by the proportionality analysis reported in chapter 5. Biomechanically, this would assist the platform divers in their execution of somersault actions during flight due to a reduced moment of inertia around a transverse axis through the center of mass.

Synchronized Swimming

Previous Studies

With the introduction of synchronized swimming as a World Championship event in Perth, we had the first opportunity to measure and report anthropometry of elite international performers. Previous studies by Hawes and Sovak (1992), Kirkendall et al. (1982), and Ross et al. (1982) have reported morphological profiles of mostly Canadian synchronized swimmers (SS). Despite the dominance of the Canadian team at the international level for many years, these results are sample-specific and do not account for multinational differences among the world's competitors.

PERCENTILE	Age	Body mass	Height	Sum of 6 skinfolds	Head girth	Relaxed arm girth	Flexed arm girth	Forearm girth	Wrist girth	Chest girth	Waist girth	Hip girth	Upper thigh girth	Calf girth	Ankle girth
P95	27.5	61.9	172.7	94.3	56.0	29.7	30.8	24.9	16.1	90.4	69.3	93.7	58.6	38.1	21.7
P90	25.8	59.6	169.2	92.1	55.8	29.1	30.0	24.6	15.8	89.7	69.2	92.8	56.1	36.1	21.6
P80	24.3	58.3	165.5	79.6	55.2	28.2	29.3	24.4	15.3	88.8	67.9	90.7	55.2	35.6	21.4
P70	22.8	56.7	164.9	68.0	54.7	27.7	28.8	24.2	15.1	87.9	67.2	89.3	54.8	35.2	21.1
P60	22.0	55.7	163.2	66.8	54.3	27.4	28.6	23.8	14.9	86.4	66.7	88.8	53.8	34.2	20.9
P50	21.8	54.9	160.9	64.2	54.1	27.1	28.3	23.6	14.8	85.7	65.8	87.8	52.3	34.0	20.4
P40	19.9	53.3	159.3	63.8	53.6	26.7	27.9	23.1	14.6	84.1	64.8	86.4	51.1	33.3	20.4
P30	18.5	51.7	158.3	57.9	52.8	25.8	27.4	22.7	14.4	83.3	64.6	84.5	50.3	32.8	19.8
P20	17.4	49.3	155.0	53.5	52.3	25.3	26.6	22.3	14.3	81.1	63.1	83.2	49.9	31.9	19.6
P10	16.6	46.9	153.7	37.2	51.1	25.0	26.1	21.8	13.9	79.8	61.7	81.8	48.2	31.1	19.5
P05	13.6	42.4	152.0	35.3	51.0	24.2	25.4	21.7	13.8	76.1	60.6	76.8	44.6	30.8	18.6
M	20.9	53.7	161.2	78.5	53.8	26.8	28.0	23.3	14.8	85.0	65.5	87.0	52.3	33.9	20.3
SD	3.8	5.5	6.0	19.4	1.6	1.7	1.7	1.1	0.6	4.3	2.5	4.7	3.5	2.0	1.0

Legend: ■——■ 1M   ▲——▲ 3M   ○- - -○ 10M

Figure 3.3 Mean body-size profiles for female divers by event. Plotted on percentiles derived from all female divers, n = 39.

(continued)

PERCENTILE	Arm span	Sitting height	Foot length	Leg length	Thigh length	Lower limb length	Hand length	Upper limb length	Femur breadth	Hand breadth	Humerus breadth	Biiliocristal breadth	AP chest breadth	Transverse chest breadth	Biacromial breadth
P95	176.7	90.9	25.1	46.2	44.2	94.8	19.5	78.4	9.2	8.2	6.7	28.4	19.8	28.4	39.1
P90	174.8	90.4	24.7	45.2	44.0	94.2	19.3	76.4	9.1	8.0	6.6	28.1	19.1	27.5	38.3
P80	169.4	89.6	24.0	44.2	43.0	91.8	19.0	74.4	8.9	7.8	6.3	27.6	18.5	27.0	37.8
P70	166.6	88.6	23.8	43.4	42.4	89.7	18.7	73.7	8.8	7.5	6.2	26.8	17.9	26.5	37.3
P60	164.4	87.7	23.5	42.8	42.0	88.8	18.3	73.1	8.6	7.4	6.0	26.5	17.5	26.3	36.8
P50	163.6	86.5	23.3	42.4	41.6	88.5	18.3	72.1	8.5	7.3	6.0	26.0	17.2	25.8	36.5
P40	162.8	85.3	22.8	41.9	41.1	87.7	17.9	71.5	8.4	7.2	5.8	25.9	16.6	25.4	36.0
P30	161.8	84.2	22.5	41.4	40.6	87.1	17.5	71.1	8.2	7.0	5.7	24.8	16.3	25.2	35.7
P20	159.4	83.5	22.4	40.6	39.3	84.8	17.4	70.0	7.9	6.7	5.5	24.2	16.0	24.9	35.5
P10	156.4	81.8	22.2	40.0	38.3	83.6	17.0	68.1	7.5	6.4	5.3	23.7	15.3	24.0	34.6
P05	155.5	81.2	21.5	39.0	37.6	80.4	17.0	67.3	7.1	6.3	5.1	23.2	14.5	23.4	33.7
M	164.4	86.3	23.2	42.5	41.4	83.8	18.2	72.3	8.4	7.3	5.9	26.0	17.2	25.8	36.5
SD	6.5	3.4	1.0	2.0	1.9	3.6	0.8	3.0	0.6	0.6	0.5	1.7	1.4	1.3	1.6

Figure 3.3 (continued)

PERCENTILE	Age	Body mass	Height	Sum of 6 skinfolds	Head girth	Relaxed arm girth	Flexed arm girth	Forearm girth	Wrist girth	Chest girth	Waist girth	Hip girth	Upper thigh girth	Calf girth	Ankle girth
P95	31.3	80.9	183.6	65.3	59.1	34.8	37.2	30.0	18.2	105.4	81.3	96.6	59.0	40.2	23.6
P90	28.4	76.7	180.9	60.4	58.5	34.3	36.7	29.3	17.9	104.1	80.6	95.9	58.6	39.4	23.4
P80	25.8	75.0	178.0	56.1	57.6	32.8	34.7	28.7	17.6	101.5	78.7	94.2	57.8	38.4	23.0
P70	24.4	73.5	175.2	52.1	57.2	32.2	34.0	28.4	17.1	98.8	76.7	93.1	56.2	38.0	22.4
P60	23.2	71.0	172.8	46.9	56.5	31.4	33.3	28.0	16.9	97.6	76.4	91.9	55.4	37.3	21.8
P50	22.1	66.6	170.4	45.1	55.8	31.0	32.5	27.5	16.6	96.2	74.9	89.8	54.5	36.5	21.5
P40	20.5	64.8	169.3	43.1	55.4	30.0	32.1	27.0	16.2	94.4	74.3	88.7	53.0	36.0	21.3
P30	19.5	63.0	168.0	37.5	55.0	29.3	31.5	26.6	16.0	92.8	72.7	87.7	52.3	35.3	20.8
P20	18.7	59.7	166.6	35.3	54.3	29.1	30.8	25.9	15.8	91.6	71.4	87.0	50.9	34.6	20.4
P10	16.1	53.8	161.0	31.3	53.5	27.1	28.4	24.0	15.4	85.3	66.4	80.8	48.4	33.6	19.9
P05	14.4	41.8	150.3	29.2	52.8	24.1	25.7	22.5	14.8	76.3	62.1	76.5	44.3	30.5	19.3
M	22.2	66.7	170.9	58.3	56.0	30.6	32.5	27.2	16.6	95.2	74.5	89.5	53.7	36.4	21.6
SD	4.6	10.2	8.6	13.7	1.9	2.8	3.0	2.1	1.0	7.3	5.1	5.8	4.2	2.5	1.3

■——— 1M   ▲——— 3M   ○- - -○ 10M

Figure 3.4 Mean body-size profiles for male divers by event. Plotted on percentiles derived from all male divers, n = 43.

(continued)

PERCENTILE	Arm span	Sitting height	Foot length	Leg length	Thigh length	Lower limb length	Hand length	Upper limb length	Femur breadth	Hand breadth	Humerus breadth	Biiliocristal breadth	AP chest breadth	Transverse chest breadth	Biacromial breadth
P95	190.3	96.8	27.8	50.9	47.5	103.7	21.2	84.0	10.3	9.2	8.0	28.6	22.0	32.3	43.4
P90	188.3	95.7	27.5	49.6	47.0	101.8	21.0	82.9	10.0	8.9	7.6	28.5	21.3	32.0	42.5
P80	186.0	93.6	26.5	48.2	46.1	99.2	20.4	81.5	9.9	8.6	7.3	28.1	20.2	31.1	41.4
P70	182.5	92.3	26.4	47.5	45.0	98.8	20.0	80.1	9.6	8.5	7.1	27.7	20.1	30.3	41.0
P60	179.8	91.5	26.2	46.9	43.9	96.6	19.6	79.2	9.5	8.4	7.0	27.5	19.6	29.4	40.6
P50	178.1	90.7	25.7	46.0	43.1	95.7	19.4	78.2	9.4	8.2	6.8	27.3	19.3	28.7	40.2
P40	175.2	89.9	25.2	45.2	42.6	92.7	19.2	77.0	9.1	8.0	6.7	26.7	19.1	28.1	39.8
P30	173.5	88.6	24.9	44.9	41.9	91.9	18.8	75.7	9.0	7.7	6.6	26.4	18.4	27.7	38.8
P20	171.6	87.3	24.1	44.1	40.7	91.4	18.5	75.3	9.0	7.6	6.4	25.1	17.7	27.2	37.9
P10	167.9	85.1	23.2	41.8	40.3	87.2	18.1	72.8	8.3	7.2	6.0	24.0	16.3	25.5	36.3
P05	156.8	79.7	22.4	40.2	37.7	82.9	17.8	68.5	8.3	6.9	5.7	23.1	15.9	23.7	34.0
M	177.7	90.3	25.5	45.9	43.2	89.1	19.4	77.9	9.3	8.1	6.8	26.7	19.1	28.8	39.7
SD	8.9	4.3	1.5	2.9	2.9	5.4	1.0	4.1	0.6	0.6	0.6	1.6	1.7	2.4	2.4

Figure 3.4 (continued)

Results

Descriptive statistics of absolute size variables for all SS are presented in Table 3.12.

Comparison Between Events

Table 3.13 summarizes the significant size differences for solo, duet, and team performers. No differences were recorded for solo and duet SS; however, the soloists were sigificantly taller and possessed longer upper and lower limb segment dimensions compared to team SS. In addition, duet performers were older than team performers. These differences are illustrated in Figure 3.5.

Best Versus Rest

Competitors who ranked in the top 10 placings for either solo or duet events were included in the Best group ($n = 25$) and compared with other solo and duet SS who formed the Rest group ($n = 18$). Few size differences were noted between groups, which suggests that elite competitors are very homogeneous in morphology. Best performers had smaller hand breadths (F = 4.22, $p < .05$) but greater sitting height (F = 5.79, $p < .05$) than the Rest. When the three Best teams were compared to the other teams, the Best were older by 1.6 yr and had greater neck, flexed arm, and midthigh girths, smaller wrist and ankle girths, greater biacromial breadth, and shorter forearm length (see Table 3.14).

Discussion

Solo and duet SS possess similar morphology, but soloists were taller and had longer limbs than team performers. These characteristics may have aesthetic advantage for soloists in addition to aiding technical execution of a variety of figures and strokes. Longer limbs assist soloists in development of lift forces using the "egg beater" kick and in sustained support sculling. The subsequent ability to hold the body out of the water is advantageous for the performance of related skills. Few size differences were noted between Best and Rest performers in the solo and duet events. However, members of the top three SS teams were more robust than members of the lower placed teams. The top three were also older, perhaps indicating longer training and experience.

Water Polo

Previous Studies

Data on male water polo players were gathered at the Mexico (de Garay et al., 1974; Hebbelinck et al., 1975), Munich (Novak et al., 1976a), and Montreal (Carter, 1982a) Olympic Games (1968, 1972, and 1976, respectively). Carter (1984a) summarized absolute size information for male water polo players (WP). Although no differences were shown for stature ($M = 179.9$ cm), de Garay et al. (1974) describe male WP ($n = 71$) as significantly heavier ($M = 77.8$ kg) than

Table 3.12   Descriptive Statistics for Synchronized Swimmers ($n = 137$)

Variable	Units	M	SD
Age	yr	20.4	2.6
Body mass	kg	56.7	5.3
Stature	cm	166.0	5.8
Sitting height	cm	88.4	3.0
Arm span	cm	170.0	6.8
Girths	cm		
Head		54.9	1.5
Neck		31.7	1.2
Arm relaxed		27.3	1.7
Arm flexed		28.4	1.6
Forearm		23.6	1.0
Wrist		14.9	0.7
Chest		88.4	3.7
Waist		66.5	3.6
Hip		91.4	4.2
Upper thigh		53.8	3.0
Middle thigh		49.0	2.7
Calf		33.3	1.6
Ankle		20.3	1.0
Breadths	cm		
Biacromial		37.2	2.0
Transverse chest		26.6	1.6
AP chest		17.6	1.4
Biiliocristal		26.8	1.7
Humerus		6.1	0.4
Wrist		5.0	0.4
Hand		7.4	0.5
Femur		8.8	0.5
Lengths	cm		
Upper limb		74.9	3.2
Arm		32.1	1.6
Forearm		24.2	1.3
Hand		18.4	0.8
Lower limb 1		77.6	3.9
Thigh 1		34.0	2.3
Leg 1		43.6	2.4
Foot		23.5	1.4

Table 3.13   ANOVA Summary of Significant Size Differences Among Synchronized Swimmers by Event (Solo n = 19; Duet n = 24; Team n = 94)

Variable	Post hoc Tukey HSD			F	p
Age	19.9 Team	20.9 Solo	21.7 Duet	5.63	.005
Stature	165.2 Team	166.4 Duet	169.0 Solo	3.60	.030
AP chest depth	17.4 Team	17.6 Solo	18.3 Duet	3.88	.020
Upper limb length	74.5 Team	75.4 Duet	76.5 Solo	3.45	.030
Arm length	31.9 Team	32.1 Duet	33.1 Solo	4.90	.010
Forearm length	24.0 Team	24.7 Duet	24.8 Solo	4.64	.010
Lower limb 1 length	77.2 Team	77.4 Duet	80.0 Solo	4.47	.010
Thigh 1 length	33.8 Team	33.9 Duet	35.7 Solo	5.84	.005
Foot length	23.4 Team	23.6 Duet	24.4 Solo	4.80	.010
Arm span	169.0 Team	170.8 Duet	173.9 Solo	4.65	.010

Note. Age in years, all other variables in centimeters.

swimmers, with greater biacromial (M = 42.2 cm) and biiliocristal (M = 29.8 cm) breadths and greater trunk length (M = 54.9 cm). Upper plus lower arm length as well as leg length were not significantly different between WP and swimmers (M = 60.4 cm and 82.6 cm, respectively). No data are available for female WP at the international level, nor has any investigation analyzed differences between playing positions in WP.

Results

Descriptive statistics of absolute size variables are presented in Table 3.15 for both male and female WP.

PERCENTILE	Age	Body mass	Height	Sum of 6 skinfolds	Head girth	Relaxed arm girth	Flexed arm girth	Forearm girth	Wrist girth	Chest girth	Waist girth	Hip girth	Upper thigh girth	Calf girth	Ankle girth
P95	25.3	65.3	175.7	121.6	57.4	29.8	30.8	25.0	16.2	95.3	72.0	99.0	59.3	36.2	22.2
P90	23.8	64.2	172.8	109.9	56.9	29.4	30.3	25.0	15.7	93.6	71.0	97.0	58.0	35.4	21.7
P80	22.1	60.9	171.5	99.4	56.2	28.7	29.6	24.4	15.4	91.3	68.9	95.3	56.6	34.7	21.2
P70	21.1	59.5	169.5	95.1	55.7	28.2	29.3	24.1	15.2	90.2	68.3	93.8	55.6	34.4	20.8
P60	20.6	58.0	167.5	89.7	55.2	27.7	29.0	23.9	15.0	89.1	67.3	92.3	54.5	33.7	20.5
P50	20.1	56.4	165.7	81.3	54.7	27.3	28.5	23.5	14.9	88.3	66.5	91.5	53.6	33.2	20.3
P40	19.4	54.9	164.2	73.8	54.4	27.0	27.9	23.3	14.7	87.3	65.9	90.4	52.8	32.8	20.1
P30	19.0	53.7	162.6	67.1	54.0	26.5	27.5	23.1	14.6	86.3	64.6	89.0	52.1	32.3	19.7
P20	18.5	52.6	160.8	60.1	53.5	26.0	27.2	22.7	14.4	85.4	63.6	87.5	51.1	32.0	19.3
P10	17.7	49.7	158.9	54.0	53.1	25.2	26.4	22.2	14.1	83.7	62.4	85.6	50.0	31.2	19.0
P05	16.6	47.8	155.8	50.1	52.4	24.6	25.7	21.7	13.8	82.0	60.9	85.1	49.5	30.7	18.7
M	20.3	56.7	166.0	98.7	54.9	27.3	28.4	23.6	14.9	88.3	66.5	91.4	53.8	33.3	20.3
SD	2.6	5.3	5.8	27.3	1.5	1.7	1.6	1.0	0.7	3.7	3.6	4.2	3.0	1.6	1.0

●——● Solo   ▲——▲ Duet   ○ - - -○ Team

(continued)

Figure 3.5   Mean body-size profiles for synchronized swimmers by event. Plotted on percentiles derived from all synchronized swimmers, n = 137.

PERCENTILE	Arm span	Sitting height	Foot length	Leg length	Thigh length	Lower limb length	Hand length	Upper limb length	Femur breadth	Hand breadth	Humerus breadth	Biiliocristal breadth	AP chest breadth	Transverse chest breadth	Biacromial breadth
P95	182.6	93.3	25.5	47.5	46.4	98.7	19.8	80.8	9.4	8.0	6.6	29.0	20.0	29.5	39.9
P90	178.0	91.9	25.2	46.8	45.7	97.2	19.4	78.8	9.3	7.9	6.6	28.6	19.5	28.7	39.6
P80	175.4	91.2	24.6	45.8	44.3	94.8	19.1	77.3	9.1	7.7	6.4	28.2	19.0	27.6	39.0
P70	173.4	90.3	24.3	45.4	43.6	93.5	18.8	76.4	9.0	7.6	6.3	27.8	18.5	27.4	38.5
P60	171.6	89.1	23.9	44.2	42.8	92.4	18.6	75.7	8.9	7.5	6.2	27.4	17.9	27.1	38.0
P50	170.4	88.7	23.5	43.6	42.2	90.7	18.5	74.9	8.8	7.4	6.1	27.0	17.7	26.6	37.5
P40	168.4	87.4	23.1	42.8	41.8	89.9	18.3	74.3	8.6	7.3	6.0	26.6	17.0	26.2	37.2
P30	166.5	86.7	22.8	42.3	41.0	88.4	18.1	73.0	8.6	7.2	6.0	25.9	16.7	25.6	36.4
P20	164.5	85.7	22.5	41.7	40.3	86.7	17.8	72.5	8.4	7.1	5.8	25.4	16.3	25.2	35.3
P10	161.2	84.4	22.0	40.2	39.1	84.7	17.4	70.8	8.2	6.9	5.6	24.2	15.7	24.2	34.4
P05	158.1	83.0	21.3	39.5	38.4	83.3	16.9	69.9	8.1	6.5	5.3	23.4	15.3	23.9	33.4
M	170.0	88.3	23.5	43.6	42.3	85.9	18.4	74.9	8.8	7.4	6.1	26.7	17.6	26.6	37.2
SD	6.7	3.0	1.4	2.4	2.3	4.3	0.8	3.3	0.5	0.5	0.4	1.7	1.4	1.6	2.0

Figure 3.5 (continued)

Table 3.14   ANOVA Summary of Significant Size Differences for Synchronized Swimmers: Best Group (Rank 1-3, *n* = 27); Rest Group (Rank 4-13, *n* = 91)

	Best		Rest			
Variable	*M*	SD	*M*	SD	F	*p*
Age	21.5	2.6	19.9	2.6	7.52	.007
Neck girth	32.1	1.0	31.5	1.2	6.21	.014
Arm flexed	29.0	1.6	28.1	1.7	6.15	.015
Wrist girth	14.5	0.6	15.0	0.7	11.49	.001
Ankle girth	19.9	0.9	20.5	1.0	6.63	.011
Biacromial breadth	38.3	1.6	36.8	2.1	12.85	.001
Forearm length	23.7	1.4	24.4	1.2	5.89	.017

Note. Age in years, all other variables in centimeters.

Comparison Between Positions

The water polo sample was partitioned according to playing position for a comparison of size variables between goalkeepers (GK), center forwards (CF), center backs (CB), and other field positions (OTH). Table 3.16 and Figure 3.6 present a summary of significant size differences for male WP. CB and CF were significantly heavier than OTH, and CF were heavier than GK. These differences in body mass are echoed for 13 girth measures and seven breadth measures; OTH were significantly smaller than CF and CB on most of these dimensions. GK did not differ from OTH on any girth measures, but were broader in biiliocristal and femur breadth dimensions.

With respect to stature however, CB, CF, and GK groups were all taller than OTH. This difference is also shown for sitting height, lower limb 1 length, and leg length. OTH have smaller upper and lower limb lengths than CB, CF, and GK, which is particularly displayed in the arm span and upper limb length variables.

A comparison of female WP by position is summarized in Table 3.17 and Figure 3.7. Female CF are significantly heavier than OTH, and this result is also reflected in seven girth and four breadth measurements. Few differences in mass or girth existed among the other positional groups. CF and GK were taller than OTH. For GK, this difference may be attributed to longer lower limb, thigh, and leg lengths, but no differences in sitting height were recorded. GK alone possessed a greater arm span and forearm length, whereas both GK and CF had longer upper limb lengths compared to OTH.

Best Versus Rest

Players comprising the semifinalist teams were included in the Best group (males, 3 teams, *n* = 37; females, 4 teams, *n* = 48); others were included in the Rest group (males *n* = 153, females *n* = 61) for this analysis. For males, only femur

Table 3.15   Descriptive Statistics for Male and Female Water Polo Players

Variable	Unit	Male water polo (n = 190) M	SD	Female water polo (n = 109) M	SD
Age	yr	25.2	3.8	23.7	3.4
Body mass	kg	86.1	8.4	64.8	7.2
Stature	cm	186.5	6.5	171.3	5.9
Sitting height	cm	97.3	3.3	90.3	3.2
Arm span	cm	196.3	7.4	174.2	6.3
Girths	cm				
Head		57.9	1.6	54.8	1.4
Neck		40.0	1.9	33.0	1.4
Arm relaxed		33.9	1.9	28.9	2.0
Arm flexed		36.4	2.0	30.2	1.8
Forearm		29.4	1.3	24.9	1.1
Wrist		17.6	0.8	15.4	0.6
Chest		107.7	4.5	90.9	3.9
Waist		84.6	4.5	69.6	3.9
Hip		98.9	4.1	95.8	5.2
Upper thigh		59.0	3.4	56.5	3.8
Middle thigh		54.9	2.9	51.4	3.3
Calf		37.9	2.2	34.9	1.9
Ankle		23.0	1.2	21.3	1.1
Breadths	cm				
Biacromial		43.1	2.1	38.1	1.6
Transverse chest		31.8	2.0	28.2	1.7
AP chest		22.4	1.7	18.9	1.5
Biiliocristal		29.4	1.6	28.4	1.6
Humerus		7.5	0.4	6.5	0.3
Wrist		6.1	0.3	5.3	0.3
Hand		8.9	0.4	7.9	0.4
Femur		10.3	0.4	9.2	0.5
Lengths	cm				
Upper limb		86.1	3.4	77.7	3.2
Arm		36.6	1.7	33.4	1.7
Forearm		28.2	1.4	25.1	1.2
Hand		21.3	1.0	19.2	0.8
Lower limb 1		89.2	4.6	81.0	3.7
Thigh 1		38.7	2.9	35.9	2.0
Leg 1		50.5	2.5	45.2	2.1
Foot		27.9	1.3	24.8	1.1

Table 3.16   ANOVA Summary of Significant Size Differences for Male Water Polo Players by Position

Variable	Post hoc Tukey HSD				F	p
Age	24.5 OTH	25.5 CB	25.8 GK	26.3 CF	2.73	.040
Body mass	82.7 OTH	86.2 GK	90.2 CF	91.4 CB	14.83	.001
Stature	184.0 OTH	188.8 CF	189.1 GK	189.2 CB	11.01	.001
Girths						
Head	57.6 OTH	57.9 GK	58.0 CB	58.5 CF	3.37	.020
Neck	39.4 GK	39.6 OTH	40.6 CB	41.0 CF	7.17	.001
Arm relaxed	33.1 GK	33.6 OTH	34.3 CB	34.8 CF	6.12	.001
Arm flexed	35.7 GK	6.0 OTH	37.1 CB	37.3 CF	6.24	.001
Forearm	29.1 OTH	29.3 GK	30.1 CB	30.1 CF	8.56	.001
Wrist	17.4 OTH	17.8 GK	18.0 CF	18.0 CB	8.13	.001
Chest	106.0 GK	106.7 OTH	109.5 CB	110.3 CF	9.92	.001
Waist	83.3 GK	83.4 OTH	86.2 CB	87.3 CF	10.04	.001
Hip	97.6 OTH	99.5 GK	99.9 CB	101.0 CF	8.19	.001
Upper thigh	58.1 OTH	59.0 GK	60.2 CB	60.3 CF	5.44	.001
Middle thigh	54.1 OTH	55.0 GK	53.9 CF	56.0 CB	5.66	.001
Calf	37.4 OTH	37.8 GK	38.6 CF	39.0 CB	5.97	.001
Ankle	22.7 OTH	23.2 GK	23.4 CF	23.2 CB	4.45	.015

Breadths

Biacromial	42.5	43.1	43.9	43.9	5.92	.001
	OTH	GK	CB	CF		
Transverse chest	31.3	31.4	32.2	32.5	4.24	.010
	GK	OTH	CB	CF		
AP chest depth	22.1	22.3	23.0	23.0	4.34	.010
	OTH	GK	CB	CF		
Biiliocristal	28.9	29.7	29.9	30.3	7.17	.001
	OTH	CF	GK	CB		
Wrist	6.0	6.2	6.2	6.2	5.11	.002
	OTH	GK	CF	CB		
Hand	8.8	9.0	9.0	9.7	7.88	.001
	OTH	GK	CB	CF		
Femur	10.1	10.4	10.4	10.5	9.01	.001
	OTH	CF	CB	GK		

Lengths

Upper limb	84.9	86.9	87.4	88.1	9.62	.001
	OTH	GK	CB	CF		
Arm	36.1	36.8	37.3	37.3	7.54	.001
	OTH	GK	CF	CB		
Forearm	27.8	28.6	28.6	28.7	5.33	.002
	OTH	CB	GK	CF		
Hand	21.2	21.9	21.6	21.6	6.49	.001
	OTH	CB	GK	CF		
Lower limb 1	87.7	90.3	90.6	91.1	7.07	.001
	OTH	CF	CB	GK		
Thigh 1	38.2	38.9	39.1	39.9	3.24	.020
	OTH	CF	CB	GK		
Leg 1	49.6	51.2	51.4	51.5	9.58	.001
	OTH	GK	CF	CB		
Foot	27.6	28.0	28.1	28.4	4.26	.010
	OTH	CB	GK	CF		
Sitting height	96.3	98.1	98.5	98.6	6.85	.001
	OTH	GK	CF	CB		
Arm span	193.4	197.8	199.5	199.9	11.75	.001
	OTH	GK	CB	CF		

Note. Age in years, body mass in kilograms, all other variables in centimeters. Sample sizes: OTH = 95, CB = 25, CF = 40, GK = 30.

PERCENTILE	Age	Body mass	Height	Sum of 6 skinfolds	Head girth	Relaxed arm girth	Flexed arm girth	Forearm girth	Wrist girth	Chest girth	Waist girth	Hip girth	Upper thigh girth	Calf girth	Ankle girth
P95	31.9	101.7	197.0	95.6	60.4	37.5	40.1	31.6	18.9	115.6	92.9	105.1	64.7	42.0	25.0
P90	30.3	97.4	194.9	86.9	59.8	36.5	39.0	31.2	18.7	114.0	90.8	104.0	63.1	41.0	24.4
P80	28.4	93.7	191.7	78.5	59.1	35.4	37.7	30.5	18.3	111.8	88.4	102.4	61.6	39.8	24.0
P70	27.1	90.2	189.4	70.7	58.6	34.6	38.2	30.2	18.1	110.0	87.0	100.8	60.6	38.8	23.6
P60	26.6	87.6	188.3	65.8	58.1	34.2	36.8	30.0	17.9	108.5	85.7	99.9	59.8	38.2	23.3
P50	24.8	85.1	186.8	62.1	57.7	33.9	36.5	29.5	17.6	107.5	84.5	99.0	59.0	38.7	23.1
P40	23.7	83.8	184.8	57.0	57.3	33.4	36.0	29.2	17.4	106.6	83.2	97.8	58.2	37.2	22.7
P30	23.0	80.7	183.0	50.4	57.0	32.9	35.2	28.7	17.2	105.4	81.6	96.8	57.2	36.6	22.2
P20	22.1	79.3	181.0	46.1	56.7	32.4	34.7	28.3	17.0	104.2	80.4	95.2	56.0	36.1	21.7
P10	20.5	75.7	177.9	39.3	55.9	31.4	34.0	27.6	16.6	101.9	78.7	93.8	54.8	35.5	21.5
P05	19.8	72.7	175.7	36.5	55.5	30.9	33.3	27.1	16.4	100.1	77.6	92.1	53.9	35.0	21.2
M	25.2	86.1	186.5	62.5	57.9	33.9	36.4	29.4	17.6	107.7	84.6	98.9	59.0	37.9	23.0
SD	3.8	6.5	6.5	17.7	1.6	1.9	2.0	1.3	0.8	4.5	4.5	4.1	3.4	2.2	1.2

● - - GK   ▲ - - - ▲ CF   △——————△ CB   ☐————☐ OTH

Figure 3.6   Mean body-size profiles for male water polo players by position. Plotted on percentiles derived from all male water polo players, *n* = 190.

(continued)

PERCENTILE	Arm span	Sitting height	Foot length	Leg length	Thigh length	Lower limb length	Hand length	Upper limb length	Femur breadth	Hand breadth	Humerus breadth	Biiliocristal breadth	AP chest breadth	Transverse chest breadth	Biacromial breadth
P95	208.1	103.0	29.9	55.3	51.5	112.3	23.1	91.8	10.9	9.7	8.2	32.1	25.5	35.2	46.7
P90	205.8	101.1	29.4	53.6	50.4	111.3	22.5	90.7	10.8	9.5	8.0	31.5	24.8	34.5	45.6
P80	202.4	99.7	28.9	52.4	49.6	108.0	22.1	88.9	10.6	9.3	7.8	30.8	24.0	33.4	44.9
P70	199.9	98.8	28.5	51.8	48.8	107.0	21.8	87.8	10.5	9.2	7.7	30.2	23.2	32.9	44.3
P60	198.1	98.1	28.1	51.0	48.1	106.1	21.5	87.1	10.4	9.0	7.6	29.8	22.6	32.3	43.8
P50	196.5	97.6	27.8	50.6	47.5	104.8	21.3	86.2	10.3	8.9	7.5	29.3	22.3	31.6	43.2
P40	195.3	96.1	27.6	49.7	46.7	102.9	21.0	85.5	10.1	8.8	7.4	29.0	22.0	31.1	42.7
P30	192.5	95.7	27.3	48.9	45.9	101.5	20.7	84.3	10.0	8.7	7.2	28.4	21.5	30.6	42.1
P20	190.1	94.5	26.9	48.2	44.9	100.1	20.4	83.2	9.9	8.6	7.1	28.0	21.0	30.0	41.3
P10	185.8	93.4	26.1	47.4	43.4	97.6	20.0	81.5	9.7	8.4	7.0	27.3	20.5	29.4	40.4
P05	183.0	91.8	26.0	46.6	42.2	95.6	19.8	79.8	9.5	8.2	6.8	26.8	19.8	28.5	39.5
M	196.3	97.3	27.9	50.5	47.2	104.2	21.3	86.1	10.3	8.8	7.5	29.4	22.4	31.8	43.1
SD	7.4	3.3	1.3	2.5	2.7	4.9	1.0	3.4	0.4	0.5	0.4	1.6	1.7	2.0	2.1

Figure 3.6   (continued)

Table 3.17   ANOVA Summary of Significant Size Differences for Female Water Polo Players by Position

Variable	Post hoc Tukey HSD				F	p
Body mass	62.3 OTH	66.0 GK	67.5 CB	69.0 CF	7.00	.001
Stature	169.4 OTH	172.4 CB	173.3 CF	175.1 GK	5.81	.001
Girths						
Chest	89.9 OTH	90.2 GK	92.8 CF	92.9 CB	5.07	.003
Waist	68.4 OTH	69.2 GK	71.5 CF	71.8 CB	5.63	.001
Hip	94.2 OTH	97.1 GK	97.9 CF	98.1 CB	4.83	.003
Upper thigh	55.4 OTH	57.6 CB	57.6 GK	58.1 CF	4.29	.010
Middle thigh	50.4 OTH	51.7 CB	52.3 GK	53.1 CF	5.24	.002
Calf	34.5 OTH	35.0 GK	35.4 CB	35.7 CF	3.15	.030
Ankle	21.0 OTH	21.4 CB	21.6 GK	21.8 CF	3.96	.010
Breadths						
Biacromial	37.6 OTH	38.1 GK	38.4 CB	39.2 CF	7.88	.001
Transverse chest	27.6 GK	27.8 OTH	28.9 CF	29.6 CB	6.56	.001
AP chest depth	18.4 GK	18.6 OTH	19.3 CB	19.5 CF	3.35	.020
Biiliocristal	28.0 OTH	28.3 GK	28.9 CB	29.2 CF	4.36	.010

Lengths

Upper limb	77.8	78.5	78.7	79.4	4.60	.005
	OTH	CB	CF	GK		
Forearm	24.7	25.3	25.5	25.7	4.86	.003
	OTH	CF	CB	GK		
Lower limb 1	79.9	81.9	82.0	83.8	5.82	.001
	OTH	CF	CB	GK		
Thigh 1	35.4	36.1	36.1	37.3	3.58	.020
	OTH	CB	CF	GK		
Leg 1	44.5	45.8	45.9	46.5	5.94	.001
	OTH	CF	CB	GK		
Foot	24.5	24.9	25.0	25.3	3.93	.010
	OTH	GK	CB	CF		
Arm span	174.2	175.6	175.9	177.4	3.99	.010
	OTH	CB	CF	GK		

Note. Body mass in kilograms, all other variables in centimeters. Sample sizes: OTH = 59, GK = 14, CB = 9, CF = 27.

breadth significantly differentiated between Best (larger) and Rest teams; for female players, the Best teams were generally composed of older players (M = 24.7 yr) than were the Rest teams (M = 23 yr). No other differences between Best and Rest performers were found, which is not surprising given the variability in size for positions within a team.

Discussion

Mean values for absolute size variables of male WP had increased from those measured in the 1968 Mexico Olympics reported by de Garay et al. (1974). The KASP WP were, on average, 2.3 yr older, 8.3 kg heavier, and 6.6 cm taller than those measured at the Mexico Games. In addition to this secular trend, a notable feature of the present data is the differentiation between field positions. In general, for both male and female WP, center players (CF and CB) were larger versions of field players (OTH). In contrast, GK were as large as CF and CB in some dimensions, but more like field players in others. Overall, GK have a unique morphology profile among water polo players.

For GK, increased stature and span helps in blocking shots, particularly to the corners of the net, and a relatively small mass could help players achieve greater height out of the water, a skill which is particularly important in this position. For CF, increased mass and stature would enable them to better maintain their position in front of the opposition goal, and increased upper limb length

(continued)

PERCENTILE	Age	Body mass	Height	Sum of 6 skinfolds	Head girth	Relaxed arm girth	Flexed arm girth	Forearm girth	Wrist girth	Chest girth	Waist girth	Hip girth	Upper thigh girth	Calf girth	Ankle girth
P95	29.8	77.2	180.4	132.0	57.1	32.7	33.8	26.9	16.4	97.4	76.0	105.3	63.5	38.3	23.3
P90	28.0	74.9	179.3	119.9	56.5	31.5	32.6	26.5	16.2	96.2	74.7	102.5	62.3	37.4	22.8
P80	26.4	71.7	176.2	109.5	55.9	30.7	31.7	25.8	15.9	94.3	73.3	100.2	60.0	36.6	22.2
P70	25.5	68.5	174.6	103.2	55.7	30.1	31.0	25.5	15.6	93.2	72.2	98.8	58.7	36.0	22.0
P60	25.0	66.5	172.4	95.7	55.1	29.3	30.6	25.1	15.5	91.8	70.4	96.6	57.3	35.5	21.4
P50	23.8	64.6	171.1	89.4	54.8	28.7	30.0	24.8	15.4	90.8	69.6	95.2	56.4	35.0	21.0
P40	23.0	61.5	169.7	81.1	54.5	28.2	29.5	24.5	15.2	89.9	68.2	93.8	55.2	34.1	20.9
P30	21.8	59.9	168.3	75.2	54.2	27.9	29.0	24.1	15.0	88.8	67.3	92.3	54.0	33.8	20.7
P20	20.5	58.7	166.9	66.2	53.6	27.1	28.5	23.8	14.9	87.8	66.2	91.2	53.0	33.4	20.5
P10	18.9	55.5	163.3	59.2	52.9	26.3	28.0	23.5	14.6	85.8	64.2	89.2	51.8	32.6	20.1
P05	18.2	54.1	161.5	53.7	52.4	26.0	27.7	23.2	14.5	84.3	63.2	88.2	51.0	31.9	19.6
M	23.7	64.8	171.3	109.1	54.8	28.9	30.2	24.9	15.4	90.9	69.6	95.8	56.5	34.9	21.3
SD	3.4	7.2	5.9	29.8	1.4	2.0	1.8	1.1	0.6	3.8	3.9	5.2	3.8	1.9	1.1

● - - ◉ GK   ▲ - - ▲ CF   ▲——▲ CB   □——□ OTH

Figure 3.7 Mean body-size profiles for female water polo players by position. Plotted on percentiles derived from all female water polo players, n = 109.

PERCENTILE	Arm span	Sitting height	Foot length	Leg length	Thigh length	Lower limb length	Hand length	Upper limb length	Femur breadth	Hand breadth	Humerus breadth	Biiliocristal breadth	AP chest breadth	Transverse chest breadth	Biacromial breadth
P95	184.1	95.5	26.4	49.0	48.5	102.0	20.7	82.8	10.0	8.5	7.1	31.1	21.5	30.9	40.8
P90	182.5	94.1	26.1	48.0	47.1	100.4	20.3	81.6	9.8	8.4	6.9	30.5	21.0	30.3	40.3
P80	180.1	93.2	25.7	47.0	45.9	98.3	19.9	80.5	9.6	8.2	6.8	29.6	20.0	29.6	39.6
P70	178.1	92.0	25.5	46.0	45.1	96.6	19.6	79.7	9.5	8.1	6.7	29.2	19.5	29.1	39.0
P60	176.3	91.2	25.1	45.7	44.7	95.4	19.4	78.5	9.3	8.0	6.6	28.8	19.0	28.6	38.5
P50	173.8	90.3	24.9	45.0	44.0	94.3	19.2	77.4	9.2	7.9	6.4	28.4	19.0	28.0	38.2
P40	172.2	89.4	24.7	44.8	43.4	93.7	19.1	76.9	9.0	7.8	6.3	28.1	18.5	27.6	37.7
P30	170.7	88.5	24.3	44.2	42.7	92.5	18.8	76.0	9.0	7.7	6.2	27.6	18.0	27.3	37.3
P20	168.6	87.3	23.9	43.3	41.7	91.0	18.6	75.2	8.9	7.6	6.1	27.1	17.5	26.9	36.6
P10	166.7	86.1	23.4	42.3	40.9	89.1	18.1	73.7	8.8	7.4	6.0	26.2	17.0	26.2	36.0
P05	163.8	85.1	22.8	41.6	39.8	87.5	18.0	72.3	8.7	7.3	6.0	25.5	16.5	25.7	35.3
M	174.2	90.3	24.8	45.2	44.0	89.2	19.3	77.7	9.2	7.9	6.5	28.4	18.8	28.2	38.1
SD	6.3	3.2	1.1	2.1	2.4	4.2	0.8	3.2	0.5	0.4	0.3	1.6	1.5	1.7	1.6

Figure 3.7 (continued)

would be an advantage in reaching and controlling passes to the front of his or her position. Similarly, increased mass and stature for CB helps these players displace and dispossess the opposing CF.

Concluding Remarks

An opportunity to observe differences in morphology for competitors within the four aquatic sports was possible due to the size and composition of the samples. Several larger size attributes were noted that could favor competitors who specialize in the various swimming strokes and event distances. Similarly, those highly ranked swimmers demonstrated specific morphological advantages compared to the rest of the competitors within the various stroke and distance categories.

In contrast to swimmers, divers showed homogeneity of absolute body size. Very few differences were noted between event specialists or between Best and Rest competitors. The synchronized swimmers who competed in the solo or duet events were also very homogeneous, with few differences between Best and Rest competitors. They differed significantly from the team SS however, particularly with respect to linear dimensions.

In water polo, players who fulfill the key positions (goalies, center backs, and center forwards) possess size attributes that are unique and may be advantageous for performing their specific functions. Distinct differences were noted for CF and CB compared to GK and OTH in both the men's and women's water polo.

Chapter 4

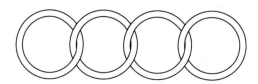

Somatotypes

J.E. Lindsay Carter and Michael J. Marfell-Jones

Somatotyping is one of several techniques used to assess the body shape and composition of athletes. The somatotype, a quantification of the present shape and composition of the human body, is expressed in a three-number rating representing endomorphy, mesomorphy, and ectomorphy components, respectively, always given in the same order (e.g., 3-5-2). Endomorphy is the relative fatness, mesomorphy is the relative musculoskeletal robustness, and ectomorphy is the relative linearity, or slenderness, of a physique. The three-number somatotype summarizes the physique independent of height and is a useful preliminary assessment of the whole body that can tell us what body types are present in various events or sports. Ratings on each component of $^1/_2$ to $2^1/_2$ are low, 3 to 5 are moderate, $5^1/_2$ to 7 are high, and $7^1/_2$ and above are very high (Carter & Heath, 1990).

Previous studies on somatotypes of athletes in a variety of sports have been summarized by Carter and Heath (1990). The studies have shown that there are often somatotype differences between sports, within sports, and by level of competition. In some sports or events only a small range of somatotypes is associated with high-level performance, whereas in others there is considerable variation and overlap in somatotype distributions. What are the somatotype characteristics of world-class swimmers, divers, synchronized swimmers, and water polo players? This chapter describes and compares the somatotypes of male and female athletes in each of the four sports by event or by playing position and performance level.

Methods

Heath-Carter somatotypes were calculated to the nearest 0.1 for each component from anthropometry using equations in Carter and Heath (1990). Endomorphy was calculated with a height correction. Because the somatotype is a three-number rating, special analyses are needed to account for this unique characteristic. PROSOMAN, a package of computer programs specifically written for somatotype analysis, was used for these analyses. The program SANOV (somatotype analysis of variance) was used to test for differences among somatotype means $(\overline{S}1 - \overline{S}n)$. SANOV was also used to test for differences among groups with respect to the dispersion (or scatter) of somatotypes about their respective means, called the somatotype attitudinal mean (SAM). Essentially, this is a test of the homogeneity of the distributions of somatotypes regardless of differences between their means. These calculations were made in three dimensions, using somatotype attitudinal distances (Carter & Heath, 1990; Carter, Ross, Duquet, & Aubry, 1983). When F-ratios reached the $p < .05$ level, post hoc Tukey tests were applied to determine which groups differed. If differences among means, $\overline{S}1 - \overline{S}n$, were significant, then the usual analysis of variance was applied to separate components to determine which ones contributed to the differences between somatotypes as a whole.

Somatotypes were plotted on a somatochart, which provides a bidimensional representation of the tridimensional somatotype. From this initial plot, the limits of the distributions were drawn on a blank somatochart used in the figures for this chapter. The PROSOMAN program CATE was used to calculate the frequencies and relative frequencies by category. Somatotypes with similar dominance relationships in the three components can be grouped into 13 categories as defined by Carter and Heath (1990). This provides for convenient verbal summaries of the distributions of different groups.

In each sport the initial subgroups by gender and by event or playing position were based on numbers in chapter 1 and Tables 1.3 through 1.6 and are the same as in other chapters. Subsequent regrouping was made on the basis of prior test results of significance. The subjects used in comparisons by performance are the same as those for other chapters.

Swimming

Previous Studies

Several studies have examined the somatotypes of swimmers at the national and international levels. Studies of male and female swimmers were made at the

Olympics in 1968 (de Garay et al., 1974; Hebbelinck et al., 1975), 1972 (Novak et al., 1976a, 1976b), and 1976 (Carter, 1984b; Carter, Aubry, & Sleet, 1982). Studies have been made on the 1948 U.S. Olympic team (Carter, 1970; Cureton, 1951), New Zealanders (Leek, 1969), Brazilians (Araujo, Pavel, & Gomes, 1978; Rocha, de Araujo, de Freitas, & Villasboas, 1977), Venezualans (Perez, 1981), Belgians (Vervaeke & Persyn, 1981), Latin Americans (Brief, 1986; Mazza et al., 1991b), and Chinese (Zeng, 1985).

With males, the results of these studies are very consistent when allowances are made for differences in methodology. The means are close to 2-5-3 for most samples. The exceptions are the greater endomorphy in the 1948 U.S. Olympians and the greater ectomorphy in the young Belgians. Comparisons by stroke show few differences, except that backstrokers (BK) were less mesomorphic and more ectomorphic than swimmers in most other strokes at the 1968 Olympics. Araujo found that the breaststroke swimmers were more mesomorphic than freestyle distance swimmers, and that the distance freestylers and backstrokers were more ectomorphic than other swimmers. With female swimmers, the samples are smaller than for males and there are few differences between strokes. The means are close to the 3-4-3, 3^1/$_2$-4-3 somatotypes. In the 1968 Olympic sample the freestyle swimmers were less mesomorphic and more ectomorphic than other groups, and breaststroke swimmers were the least endomorphic. This latter difference was also found in Araujo's Brazilian sample. The majority of male swimmers are either balanced mesomorphs or ectomesomorphs, and the majority of female swimmers are central somatotypes.

Results

Swimmer somatotypes were analyzed by primary stroke and distance. Because there were 11 initial event groups for each gender, comparisons were made first within each stroke to reduce the groups for analysis.

Males

Descriptive statistics by stroke and distance are shown in Table 4.1. The limits of the somatotype distributions for all swimmers and means for the stroke groups are plotted in Figure 4.1

The mean somatotype (rounded) for all swimmers was 2-5-3 in the ectomeso-morphy sector of the somatochart. Ectomesomorphs are characterized by low relative fatness, moderate-to-high musculoskeletal robustness, and moderate linearity. Some contrast between the long distance (LD) and 200-m backstroke (BK) swimmers was noted in the frequencies: the LD were more endomesomorphic and the BK were more ectomesomorphic. The majority (80%) of the other swimmers were balanced mesomorphs (20%) or ectomesomorphs (60%). Overall, 78% of all swimmers were in these two categories, with ectomesomorphy being the largest single category (58%).

Comparisons Within Stroke.

The 11 initial event groups consisted of four in freestyle (FR), two each in breaststroke (BR), backstroke (BK), and butterfly (FL), and one in individual

Table 4.1   Somatotype Characteristics of Male Swimmers by Stroke and Distance

Event	N	Component	M	SD	Low	High
Freestyle						
50 + 100 m	47	Endo	1.7	0.3	1.0	2.6
		Meso	4.9	0.9	3.2	6.8
		Ecto	3.2	0.9	1.5	5.3
200 + 400 m	34	Endo	1.9	0.5	1.2	3.0
		Meso	4.7	0.8	3.1	7.0
		Ecto	3.1	0.8	1.0	4.7
1500 m	10	Endo	1.5	0.4	1.0	2.3
		Meso	4.8	0.6	4.1	5.8
		Ecto	3.4	0.5	2.3	3.9
Total	91	Endo	1.8	0.4	1.0	3.0
		Meso	4.8	0.9	3.1	7.0
		Ecto	3.2	0.8	1.0	5.3
Long distance	13	Endo	2.5	0.7	1.4	3.9
		Meso	5.3	0.8	3.8	6.3
		Ecto	2.3	0.9	1.3	3.8
Breaststroke						
50 + 100 m	25	Endo	1.8	0.5	1.0	3.1
		Meso	5.1	1.0	2.9	6.6
		Ecto	2.9	0.6	1.8	3.9
200 m	12	Endo	2.1	1.0	1.3	4.9
		Meso	5.7	1.0	4.8	7.8
		Ecto	2.6	0.7	1.5	3.8
Total	37	Endo	1.9	0.7	1.0	3.1
		Meso	5.3	1.0	2.9	7.8
		Ecto	2.8	0.7	1.5	3.9
Backstroke						
50 + 100 m	15	Endo	1.8	0.4	1.1	2.9
		Meso	5.2	0.7	4.0	6.4
		Ecto	3.1	0.5	2.0	4.3
200 m	13	Endo	1.9	0.5	1.3	2.9
		Meso	4.3	0.8	2.9	5.3
		Ecto	3.5	0.5	2.9	4.7
Total	28	Endo	1.8	0.4	1.1	2.9
		Meso	4.8	0.9	2.9	6.4
		Ecto	3.3	0.6	2.0	4.7
Butterfly						
50 + 100 m	24	Endo	2.1	0.7	1.3	3.9
		Meso	5.5	1.0	4.2	8.1
		Ecto	2.5	0.9	0.5	3.7

Event	N	Component	M	SD	Low	High
200 m	17	Endo	2.0	0.8	1.3	4.5
		Meso	5.2	0.9	3.9	6.4
		Ecto	2.5	0.7	1.5	3.8
Total	41	Endo	2.0	0.7	1.3	4.5
		Meso	5.4	0.9	3.9	8.1
		Ecto	2.5	0.8	0.5	3.8
Individual medley						
200 + 400 m	21	Endo	1.9	0.5	1.0	2.9
		Meso	4.9	0.7	3.1	5.9
		Ecto	3.0	0.6	2.0	4.2
Total	231	Endo	1.9	0.6	1.0	4.9
		Meso	5.0	0.9	2.9	8.1
		Ecto	2.9	0.8	0.5	5.3

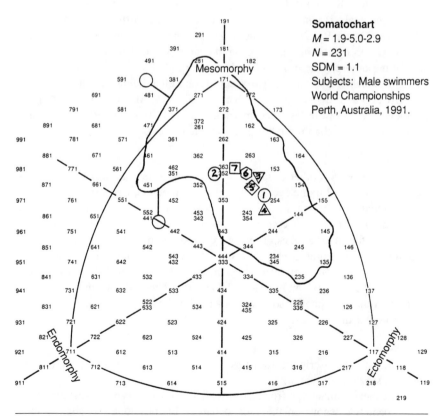

Figure 4.1 Limits of the somatotype distribution for male swimmers, with somatoplots of means for stroke groups. Key: 1 = 50-1500 m freestyle; 2 = long distance; 3 = 50-100 m backstroke; 4 = 200 m backstroke; 5 = individual medley; 6 = breaststroke; 7 = butterfly.

medley (IM) (see Table 4.1). SANOV analysis showed no differences between event groups wthin FR, BR, BK, or FL in the scatter of somatotypes about their means (SAM). There were no differences between mean somatotypes ($\overline{S}$) in BR (F = 2.907) or FL (F = 0.654), therefore the distance groups were combined for further analysis. Among the four freestyle groups, the long distance swimmers (LD) were different from the other three groups, F(3,100) = 4.385, $p < .01$. Therefore, the groups 50 + 100 m, 200 + 400 m, and 1500 m were combined. When compared to the combined group, LD were more endomorphic, t = 5.68, $p < .01$, and less ectomorphic, t = −3.78, $p < .01$. In BK the mean somatotypes differed, F(1,26) = 7.329, $p < .05$. The 200 m swimmers (BK 200) were less mesomorphic than the 50 + 100 m swimmers (BK 50 + 100), t = −3.29, $p < .01$. Although the t-ratio for ectomorphy was 2.38 ($p < .05$), it did not quite reach the $p < .017$ level required for the Bonferoni adjustment for three t-tests. Therefore, the stroke and distance groups were reduced from 11 to 7.

Comparisons by Stroke and Distance.

Comparisons using SANOV showed no differences between the seven groups (FR, LD, BR, BK 50 + 100, BK 200, FL, and IM) in SAMs (F = 1.508, df = 6,224). The analysis among means ($\overline{S}$) showed that LD differed (F = 5.322, $p < .01$) from FR and BK 200, and the latter also differed from BR and FL. One-way ANOVAs by component were significant at $p < .001$ for endomorphy (F = 3.925), mesomorphy (F = 4.342), and ectomorphy (F = 7.492). LD were more endomorphic than all other groups except FL, as well as being more mesomorphic than BK 200 and less ectomorphic than BK 200, IM, BK 50 + 100, and FR. In addition, BK 200 were less mesomorphic than BK 50 + 100, BR, and FL and more ectomorphic than the latter pair (see Figure 4.1).

Best Versus Rest.

For consistency with other chapters, "Best" was defined as all swimmers who placed 1 through 12 in the event; "Rest" were all others. Because some athletes were entered in different strokes, they could appear in two or three analyses. The eight groups used for comparisons were the four freestyle groups and one for each of the other strokes. There were no differences in mean somatotypes within any of the eight groups. However, there were differences in the scatter of somatotypes about their respective means (SAMs) in the 50 + 100 m FR, F(1,56) = 4.825, $p < .05$, and in BR, F(1,37) = 10.26, $p < .01$. The most successful in these events had smaller somatotype variations than the less successful; there were no other differences.

Females

Table 4.2 shows descriptive statistics by stroke and distance, as well as totals for each stroke and overall.

The mean somatotype (rounded) for all swimmers was 3-4-3 (the upper part of the central category on the somatochart). This physique has slightly more musculoskeletal robustness than either relative fatness or linearity, which are equal. Overall, the swimmers were in 11 out of 13 categories, but 93% were in 8 categories. The greatest concentrations were in the central (23.5%), balanced mesomorph (14.1%), and endomesomorph (14.1%) categories. There were slightly more somatotypes (38.8%) to the right of central and balanced mesomorph categories than to the left (23.5%). Eight out of 10 LD were left of center in the more endomorphic categories. When the relative frequencies were calculated without LD, the percentage to the right of center increased slightly to 39.8% and decreased to the left of center to 20.1%. Somatotype means and distribution limits are plotted in Figure 4.2.

Comparisons Within Stroke.

Comparisons were made using the same groups for males. There were no differences within stroke between SAMs, or means ($\overline{S}$), except for freestyle. The S for LD was different from the other three event groups—which did not differ among themselves, $F(3,70) = 7.454$, $p < .01$. LD were significantly (all $p < .001$) greater in endomorphy and mesomorphy and lower in ectomorphy than the combined group of three freestyle events. Thus, 11 groups were reduced to 6 for further analysis.

Comparisons by Stroke and Distance.

When the six groups (FR, LD, BR, BK, FL, and IM) were compared, the SANOV analysis showed that there were no differences in SAMs, $F(5,164) = 1.505$, but there were differences in mean somatotypes between LD and the other five groups who did not differ among themselves, $F = 5.265$, $p < .01$. The F-ratios for all three components were significant (all $p < .008$). LD showed greater endomorphy and lower ectomorphy than all other strokes and were more mesomorphic than BK, IM, and FR (see Figure 4.2).

Best Versus Rest.

The event groups compared were the same for the males, except that 800 m FR replaced 1500 m FR. There were no differences between the Best and Rest in SAMs for any stroke. Also, there were no differences in mean somatotype within a stroke, except for LD. Although the number of LD in each group was small (Best = 4, Rest = 6), $F = 7.492$ was significant ($p < .05$), with means of 3.5-3.9-2.6 and 5.0-5.3-1.0, respectively. The Best were less mesomorphic, $t = 3.23$, $p < .02$ and more ectomorphic, $t = 3.79$, $p < .01$, than the Rest, but did not differ on endomorphy, $t = 2.05$.

Discussion

Males

Except for the LD and BK 200 groups, the male swimmers are fairly similar both between and within each stroke and distance. LD are more endomesomorphic than all other groups, and BK 200 are more ectomesomorphic than some of the other groups. The difference between the short- and long-distance BK calls for

Table 4.2   Somatotype Characteristics of Female Swimmers by Stroke and Distance

Event	N	Component	M	SD	Low	High
Freestyle						
50 + 100 m	31	Endo	2.8	0.9	1.6	5.9
		Meso	3.7	1.0	1.3	6.0
		Ecto	3.2	1.0	0.8	5.2
200 + 400 m	27	Endo	2.9	0.5	1.5	3.8
		Meso	3.7	0.8	2.2	6.2
		Ecto	3.2	0.8	1.5	5.0
800 m	6	Endo	2.4	0.5	1.7	3.0
		Meso	3.8	0.4	3.0	4.2
		Ecto	3.0	0.5	2.6	3.8
Total	64	Endo	2.8	0.7	1.5	5.9
		Meso	3.7	0.9	1.3	6.2
		Ecto	3.2	0.9	0.8	5.2
Long distance	10	Endo	4.4	1.3	2.2	6.4
		Meso	4.7	1.0	3.4	6.2
		Ecto	1.7	1.0	0.1	3.4
Breaststroke						
50 + 100 m	16	Endo	2.6	1.3	1.5	6.7
		Meso	3.9	0.9	2.4	5.9
		Ecto	3.3	1.0	1.0	4.9
200 m	12	Endo	2.9	0.8	1.7	4.0
		Meso	4.3	1.0	2.3	6.2
		Ecto	2.8	0.7	1.9	4.5
Total	28	Endo	2.7	1.1	1.5	6.7
		Meso	4.1	1.0	2.3	6.2
		Ecto	3.1	0.9	1.0	4.9
Backstroke						
50 + 100 m	8	Endo	2.6	0.6	1.7	3.5
		Meso	3.5	0.4	3.0	4.2
		Ecto	3.6	0.5	3.0	4.7
200 m	10	Endo	2.5	0.4	1.8	3.2
		Meso	3.7	0.7	2.7	4.6
		Ecto	3.1	0.9	1.8	4.7
Total	18	Endo	2.5	0.5	1.7	3.5
		Meso	3.6	0.6	2.7	4.6
		Ecto	3.4	0.8	1.8	4.7
Butterfly						
50 + 100 m	16	Endo	2.8	0.9	1.8	4.3
		Meso	3.9	1.1	1.6	5.5
		Ecto	3.1	0.9	1.7	4.5

Event	N	Component	M	SD	Low	High
200 m	13	Endo	3.0	0.6	2.2	4.0
		Meso	4.2	0.9	3.0	6.3
		Ecto	2.8	0.9	1.4	4.1
Total	29	Endo	2.9	0.8	1.8	4.3
		Meso	4.0	1.0	1.6	6.3
		Ecto	3.0	0.9	1.4	4.5
Individual medley						
200 + 400 m	21	Endo	2.9	0.9	1.5	4.7
		Meso	3.7	1.0	1.5	5.5
		Ecto	3.0	0.8	1.7	4.4
Total	170	Endo	2.9	0.9	1.5	6.7
		Meso	3.9	1.0	1.3	6.3
		Ecto	3.0	0.9	0.1	5.2

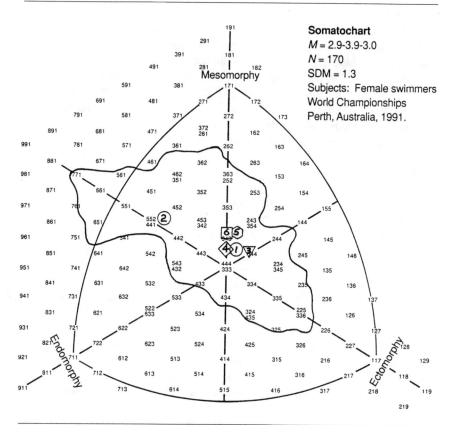

Somatochart
M = 2.9-3.9-3.0
N = 170
SDM = 1.3
Subjects: Female swimmers
World Championships
Perth, Australia, 1991.

Figure 4.2   Limits of the somatotype distribution for female swimmers, with soma-toplots of means for stroke groups. Key: 1 = 50-800 m freestyle; 2 = long distance; 3 = backstroke; 4 = individual medley; 5 = breaststroke; 6 = butterfly.

further analysis to determine its importance. The mean somatotype for IM was found to be in the center of the means for all strokes, a predictable conclusion with swimmers who have to swim proficiently in all four strokes.

The overall mean for the swimmers is 1.9-5.0-2.9; without LD ($N = 13$) the mean is still very close at 1.9-5.0-3.0. It was expected that the Best in each stroke would have different somatotypes than the Rest. However, this was not the case. There were no differences between means, although the Rest did have greater dispersions about their means than the Best in 50 + 100 m FR and BR. This suggests that for these strokes some of the less successful competitors had quite different physiques from the more successful. These differences might be related to their poorer performance, but this cannot be inferred from these data alone.

Although the somatotypes are scattered over a larger area to the left of the balanced mesomorphy category, there are only 19 swimmers (8%) in the area (see Figure 4.1): five LD, seven FL, three BR, and one each in FR and IM. In spite of differences between LD and BK 200, all LD except one fall within the distribution limits of all other swimmers. This illustrates the overlap in distributions among strokes.

When compared to the 1968 and 1976 Olympic data, the 1991 swimmers were very similar in means and in range of component values. The 1991 sample is the first to include LD. Their mean is closer to that of the 1948 USA Olympic team ($\overline{S}$ = 2.9-5.4-2.7) than to other samples (Carter & Heath, 1990). The present sample is almost four times larger than the 1968 sample and is even larger than samples in other studies. Therefore, considerable confidence can be placed in the results of comparisons within and between strokes. However, most of the present findings are consistent with previous studies.

Females

LD were more endomesomorphic than all other groups, with a mean clearly separate from them. Mean somatotypes for the other four strokes are close and quite homogeneous in their distributions. The overall mean was 2.9-3.9-3.0; without the 10 LD, 2.8-3.8-3.1. LD is the only event with differences between Best ($\overline{S}$ = 3.5-3.9-2.6) and Rest ($\overline{S}$ = 5.0-5.3-1.0). The Best are closer to the mean of the other swimmers, whereas the Rest are much more endomorphic. Although the LD sample is small, ours is the first study to include their somatotype differences. In contrast to male BK, there are no differences between the short- and longer distance BK.

With regard to somatotype distributions, all strokes except LD have some somatoplots in the southeast or ectomorphic sector of the somatochart. Furthermore, there are five somatoplots to the far west, outside the 1-7-1 to 7-1-1 arc: three LD and one each from FR and BR. Although the area outlined to the left of the central category is quite large, it contains only 23.5% of all somatotypes (see Figure 4.2).

The combined mean for the 1968 and 1976 Olympic samples ($n = 59$) was 3.2-3.9-3.0. The 1991 sample, $\overline{S}$ = 2.8-3.8-3.1 (without LD), appears to be slightly more ectomesomorphic. Both means are in the upper central category, but more somatotypes have higher endomorphy in the former than in the latter, which has higher ectomorphy. These findings suggest a slight downward trend in endomorphy for present-day swimmers. In addition, the 1991 sample is slightly less endomorphic and ectomorphic than the South American samples cited in the introduction.

Summary

The average somatotype for male swimmers is 2-5-3, an ectomesomorph, with the majority of somatotypes in this category or in balanced mesomorphy. There are no differences within or between strokes, except for LD and BK, and some greater variation in the less successful sprint FR and in BR. LD are more endomesomorphic than other swimmers, and 200 m BK are more ectomesomorphic than all others except IM. There does not appear to be any change in the average somatotype of male swimmers since the 1968 Olympics.

The female swimmer has a somatotype of 3-4-3, an upper central somatotype. Most swimmers are in the central somatotype category with slightly more in the ectomorphic than in the endomorphic categories. LD are much more endomesomorphic than other swimmers, although the most successful are closer to the others. The present study shows that swimmers are slightly less endomorphic than those in previous studies.

Diving

Previous Studies

Divers were somatotyped at the Mexico City Olympics in 1968 (de Garay et al., 1974), and at the Montreal Olympics in 1976 (Carter et al., 1982b), the small numbers of which were combined (Carter, 1984b). The anthropometric somatotype (with height-corrected endomorphy) was 3.1-4.1-2.9 for females ($n = 8$) and 1.9-5.5-2.7 for males ($n = 20$). Female divers were mostly central somatotypes; males were mostly balanced mesomorphs or ectomesomorphs. The 1-m springboard was not included as an event in these Olympics.

Results

For analysis by event, the divers were separated by gender and grouped according to primary event: 1 m (1M), 3 m (3M), or 10 m platform (10M). For analysis by performance level, those who placed from 1 to 10 in any of the three events were designated Best divers; those who placed 11th or lower were designated as Rest. Table 4.3 gives descriptive statistics by primary event and for female and male divers, and Figure 4.3 plots the limits of the somatotype distributions and means for primary events.

Females

The average somatotype for female divers ($n = 39$) was 3-4-3 (rounded), that is, a central somatotype with mesomorphy slightly higher than both endomorphy and

Table 4.3   Somatotype Characteristics of Female and Male Divers by Primary Event

Event	N		Somatotype	HWR[a]	SAM[b]
Females					
1M	13	M	3.2-4.3-2.4	42.3	1.3
		SD	0.7 1.0 1.0	1.4	0.7
3M	9	M	2.9-3.6-2.5	42.5	1.4
		SD	0.5 1.1 0.9	1.3	0.5
10M	17	M	2.5-3.6-3.2	43.4	1.2
		SD	0.8 0.8 0.7	1.0	0.4
Total	39	M	2.8-3.8-2.8	42.8	1.3
		SD	0.7 1.0 0.9	1.3	0.6
Males					
1M	19	M	1.9-5.5-2.3	42.1	1.1
		SD	0.5 1.0 0.8	1.2	0.8
3M	10	M	2.0-5.3-2.3	42.2	1.1
		SD	0.5 0.9 0.7	1.0	0.4
10M	14	M	2.0-5.1-2.7	42.8	1.2
		SD	0.6 0.9 0.7	0.9	0.4
Total	43	M	2.0-5.3-2.4	42.4	1.1
		SD	0.5 1.0 0.8	1.1	0.6

[a]HWR = height to cube root weight ratio; [b]SAM = somatotype attitudinal mean.

ectomorphy. The application of SANOV showed that there were no differences between mean somatotypes by event, $F_{(2,36)} = 3.03$, or for SAMs, F = 0.43. We analyzed the somatotype distribution for frequencies in somatotype categories. For simplicity, we grouped the categories from left to right across the somatochart into mesomorph-endomorph plus endomesomorph, balanced mesomorph plus central, and ectomesomorph plus mesomorph-ectomorph plus mesoectomorph plus others. The somatotypes, fairly evenly distributed across these categories, were 33%, 39%, and 28%, respectively. The mean somatotypes using all competitors in each event were: 1M = 3.0-4.2-2.5 (n = 19), 3M = 2.9-3.9-2.6 (n = 21), and 10M = 2.7-3.7-3.0 (n = 19).

Best Versus Rest.

The mean somatotype of the Best (n = 19) divers was 2.8-4.0-3.0, with standard deviations (SDs) of 0.7, 1.1, and 0.8; the mean for the less successful divers (n = 20) was 2.9-3.7-2.6 (SDs = 0.8, 0.9, and 0.9). There were no differences between means, $F_{(1,37)} = 0.97$, or SAMs, F = 0.21. When the Best and Rest divers were grouped according to somatotype categories (see preceding) they were similarly distributed with 32%, 36%, and 32% for the Best and 35%, 40%, and 25% for the Rest.

Somatochart

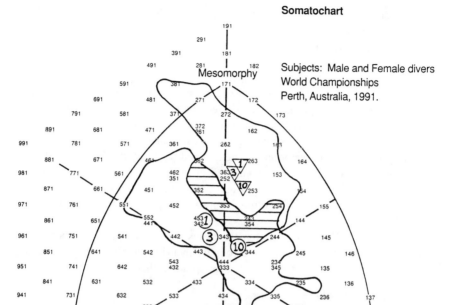

Figure 4.3 Limits of the somatotype distribution for male (upper) and female (lower) divers. Means for the primary events, 1M, 3M, and 10M, are enclosed by triangles for males and circles for females. Hatching shows area of overlap.

Males

The average somatotype (rounded) for male divers ($n = 43$) was $2\text{-}5^1/_2\text{-}2^1/_2$, that is, a balanced mesomorph, with mesomorphy much higher than endomorphy and ectomorphy, which are both low. There were no differences between mean somatotypes by event, $F(2,40) = 0.84$, or for SAMs, $F = 0.005$. All divers, except one (a mesomorph-ectomorph), were in either the endomesomorphy (21%), balanced mesomorphy (28%), or ectomesomorphy (49%) categories. The mean somatotypes, using all competitors in each event, were: 1M = 2.0-5.4-2.3 ($n = 28$); 3M = 2.0-5.4-2.4 ($n = 26$); and 10M = 2.0-5.3-2.5 ($n = 20$).

Best Versus Rest.

The mean somatotype for the best divers was 1.9-5.4-2.5 (Sds = 0.6, 0.9, and 0.7), for the rest, 2.0-5.3-2.4 (SDs = 0.5, 1.0, and 0.8). There were no differences between means, $F(1,41) = 0.27$, or between SAMs, $F = 0.41$. The relative frequencies in somatotype categories for the Best versus Rest were 16% and 25% endomesomorphs, 32% and 25% balanced mesomorphs, and 53% and 46% ectomesomorphs, respectively.

Discussion

Both male and female divers had consistent somatotypes across events in both their average somatotype and their scatter about the means. Among events, variation in endomorphy is lower than for mesomorphy or ectomorphy. There is a tendency for 10M to be slightly more linear than other divers. Somatotype similarity by event and performance is explained partly by the fact that 44% of female and 58% of male divers competed in more than one event. The main elements of somersaulting, twisting, flight path, and body position are common to all three events in diving. Therefore, it appears logical that similar somatotypes would be successful.

As shown in Figure 4.3, the female means tend to be slightly further apart than the male means. Both areas are roughly oval in shape and parallel to the ectomorphic axis, and there is a small overlap along their adjacent borders.

Medalists Versus Others

There were six medalists in both male and female samples. The medalists had mean somatotypes close to their respective sex means: females $\bar{S}$ = 2.7-4.0-2.9 and males $\bar{S}$ = 2.4-5.3-2.4. The range of somatotypes (rounded) for females ranged from $3^{1}/_{2}$-5-$2^{1}/_{2}$ (middle endomesomorphy) to a 3-2-4, the lowest on the somatochart. Males ranged from a 3-$7^{1}/_{2}$-$^{1}/_{2}$ (upper left) to a $1^{1}/_{2}$-$4^{1}/_{2}$-3 (lower right) on the somatochart.

When the present divers are compared to those from previous Olympic studies (Carter, 1984b), they are similar in mean somatotype. But there is a wider spread of somatotypes in this study to the right and left of the previous Olympic distributions—perhaps due in part to a greater number of divers and the addition of the 1M event in Perth, 1991.

Summary

The average somatotype for female divers is close to 3-4-3. There are no differences among events or between Best and other divers. For male divers the average somatotype is close to 2-$5^{1}/_{2}$-$2^{1}/_{2}$, with no difference by event or Best versus Rest.

Synchronized Swimming

Previous Studies

Ross, Corlett, Drinkwater, Faulkner, and Vajda (1977) found a mean somatotype of 3.5-3.3-3.3 for 145 competitors in all events at the 1977 Canadian Championships. The elite competitors (n = 17), with a somatotype of 3.4-3.3-3.3, were somewhat leaner, about the same in muscularity, and somewhat more linear than a reference group. After reviewing the data, a mean of 3.3-3.6-3.4 (n = 136) was reported by Ross et al. (1982).

Results

The synchronized swimmers (SS) were grouped for analysis into their primary events: solo, duet, or team only. In addition, comparisons were made among the 13 countries that entered the team competition. For each country, we included all athletes who designated "team" as one of their three events. This procedure resulted in numbers ranging from 7 for China to 10 for five countries, with other countries in between. In solo and duet events, those athletes placing 1 through 10 were designated Best, those placing 11 and lower were designated Rest. In all events combined routine and figure scores determined final placement.

Descriptive statistics for each primary event for all SS and for teams are given in Tables 4.4 and 4.5, respectively. The mean somatotype (rounded) for all SS was $3^1/_2$-$3^1/_2$-3, that is, a central somatotype with slightly more endomorphy and mesomorphy than ectomorphy. The four somatotype categories to the left of center on the somatochart (in which endomorphy and mesomorphy combinations are high and ectomorphy is low) account for 31% of all SS. Another 35% are in the central and balanced mesomorphy categories, and 24% are to the right of the center in ectomesomorphy through balanced ectomorphy categories. Finally, 10% of the somatotypes are in the lower sector of the somatochart where mesomorphy is lower than both endomorphy and ectomorphy.

Comparisons Among Events

There were no differences between primary event mean somatotypes, $F(2,134) = 1.57$, or between SAMs, $F(2,134) = 1.08$. The limits of the somatotype distribution of all SS, as well as those for solo and duet events, are shown in Figure 4.4

The somatochart shows the overlap in the distributions of solo and duet competitors. Six out of 24 (25%) of those in duet are more endomorphic and mesomorphic (i.e., to the left on the somatochart) and do not overlap with the plots of the soloists. The soloists, most restricted in their somatoplots, show only

Table 4.4   Somatotype Characteristics of Synchronized Swimmers by Primary Event

Event	N		Somatotype	HWR[a]	SAM[b]
Solo	19	M	3.0-3.3-3.6	43.9	1.2
		SD	0.7 0.7 0.8	1.1	0.6
Duet	24	M	3.6-3.6-3.1	43.3	1.4
		SD	1.0 1.0 0.8	1.1	0.7
Team	94	M	3.3-3.5-3.1	43.2	1.4
		SD	1.0 0.9 1.0	1.4	0.8
Total	137	M	3.3-3.5-3.1	43.3	1.4
		SD	1.0 0.9 1.0	1.3	0.8

[a]HWR = height to cube root weight ratio; [b]SAM = somatotype attitudinal mean.

Table 4.5   Somatotype Characteristics of Synchronized Swimmers According to Place in the Team Event

Team	Place	N	Component	M	SD	Low	High
USA	1	10	Endo	3.4	0.6	2.2	4.4
			Meso	3.8	0.9	2.1	4.8
			Ecto	2.8	0.7	2.0	3.9
Canada	2	9	Endo	3.2	0.7	1.8	4.1
			Meso	3.3	0.8	2.3	4.6
			Ecto	3.1	0.7	1.6	4.1
Japan	3	8	Endo	3.0	0.5	2.3	3.8
			Meso	3.8	0.4	3.3	4.5
			Ecto	2.9	0.3	2.3	3.3
USSR	4	9	Endo	2.8	0.9	1.8	4.2
			Meso	3.4	0.6	2.4	4.3
			Ecto	3.5	1.0	1.6	4.7
France	5	9	Endo	3.4	0.9	1.9	4.9
			Meso	3.4	0.6	2.2	4.3
			Ecto	3.4	0.8	2.6	5.3
China	6	7	Endo	4.4	0.7	2.9	5.0
			Meso	3.7	0.5	3.0	4.3
			Ecto	2.7	0.5	2.1	3.5
Italy	7	10	Endo	3.5	0.9	1.5	4.7
			Meso	3.9	0.5	3.3	4.9
			Ecto	2.6	0.7	1.6	3.8
Britain	8	9	Endo	3.4	0.7	2.6	4.5
			Meso	3.5	0.4	2.5	4.1
			Ecto	2.7	1.0	0.4	3.9
Netherlands	9	10	Endo	3.6	1.4	1.5	5.5
			Meso	3.1	0.8	2.0	4.0
			Ecto	3.8	1.3	2.5	6.6
Switzerland	10	10	Endo	3.3	1.0	1.8	4.8
			Meso	3.2	1.2	1.3	5.4
			Ecto	3.6	1.2	1.7	5.3
Australia	11	9	Endo	3.8	0.9	2.5	4.9
			Meso	4.1	0.9	3.0	5.6
			Ecto	3.1	1.0	1.3	4.3
Spain	12	8	Endo	2.3	1.0	1.0	4.8
			Meso	4.1	0.9	3.0	5.6
			Ecto	3.1	1.0	1.3	4.3

Team	Place	N	Component	M	SD	Low	High
New Zealand	13	10	Endo	3.2	1.1	2.0	5.7
			Meso	2.4	1.2	0.7	4.8
			Ecto	3.2	1.4	0.1	4.9
Total	1-13	118	Endo	3.3	1.0	1.5	5.7
			Meso	3.5	0.9	0.7	5.6
			Ecto	3.2	1.0	0.1	6.6

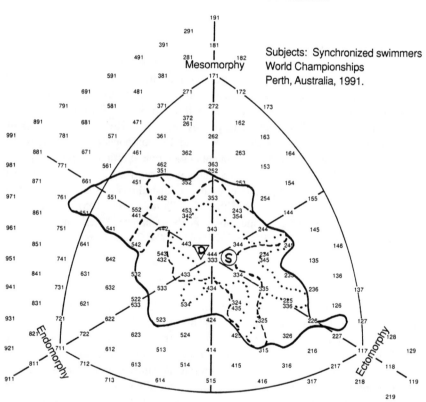

Somatochart

Subjects: Synchronized swimmers
World Championships
Perth, Australia, 1991.

Figure 4.4 Limits of the somatotype distribution for all synchronized swimmers. Solo competitors are enclosed by a dotted line and their mean by a circle, S = 3.0-3.3-3.6. Duet competitors are enclosed by a dashed line and their mean by a triangle, D = 3.6-3.6-3.1.

two with an endomorphy rating above 3.6. Both solo and duet swimmers were within the distribution of those entered only in the team event. Although these groups are based on primary event, 63% of solo and duet swimmers were in more than one event.

Best Versus Rest—Solo and Duet

Out of the 43 SS in these two events, 25 were ranked 1 through 10 (Best) in either or both events, including all medalists in both events. The average somatotypes ($\overline{S}$) for the Best and Rest were $\overline{S}$ = 3.4-3.6-3.2 (SDs = 0.8, 0.7, and 0.8), and $\overline{S}$ = 3.3-3.2-3.5 (SDs = 1.0, 1.1, and 0.8), respectively. These means were not different, F(1,41) = 1.15, nor were SAMs F(1,41) = 1.62.

Comparisons Among Teams

Of the 13 teams entered, at least eight members of each team were somatotyped except for China (n = 7). The means for each team according to place and their somatoplots are shown in Table 4.5 and Figure 4.5, respectively. Because of the need to reduce the large number of possible comparisons and the limitation that only 10 groups could be entered at one time into the SANOV program, several groupings of teams were examined according to place in the competition. The F-ratios for teams placed 1 through 5, 6 through 8, and 9 through 13 were not significant for either mean somatotypes or SAMs. However, a number of differences between means were greater than 1.0 component units, suggesting that some differences between components taken one at a time might be significant. One-way ANOVAS using all 13 teams were run for each component. The Spanish were less endomorphic than both the Australians and the Chinese, and the Soviets were less endomorphic than the Chinese, F(11,105) = 2.322, p < .011. New Zealanders were less mesomorphic than Chinese, Americans, Japanese, Italians, and Spanish, F(11,105) = 2.649, p < .004. There were no differences in ectomorphy.

Discussion

There is a wide range of somatotypes in world-class SS. No differences were found in either mean somatotypes or their dispersions by team, or between Best and others in solo and duet events. Furthermore, there were no differences by whole somatotype among teams, although separate component analysis revealed that there were some differences in endomorphy and mesomorphy. These similarities may be due to the fact that almost half (47%) of soloists were also in a duet secondary event. Also, 53% of soloists and 63% of duetists were in the team event. Seven soloists were not entered in another event, but only two of them belonged to countries that had team entries. These data show that the somatotypes are similar across events, suggesting that successful body types in the sport can compete in any of the three events, provided they have the required skill level (especially in solo and duet events).

Examination of team statistics shows that the Chinese and Japanese teams have the smallest SD (0.3-0.7) for the three components, whereas the range is

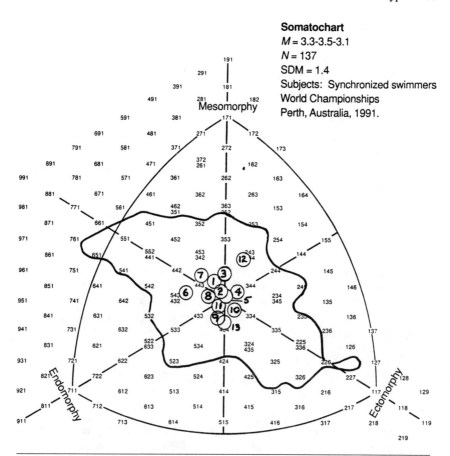

Figure 4.5 Limits of the somatotype distribution for all synchronized swimmers. Means for each team are plotted by place. Key: 1 = USA; 2 = Canada; 3 = Japan; 4 = USSR; 5 = France; 6 = China; 7 = Italy; 8 = Britain; 9 = Netherlands; 10 = Switzerland; 11 = Australia; 12 = Spain; 13 = New Zealand.

from 0.9 through 1.4 for the Swiss, Spanish, and New Zealand teams. The means for the first five teams are fairly close to the center of the somatochart, but so are those for Great Britain, Switzerland, and Australia. The outliers are Italy, China, Holland, Spain, and New Zealand. Of the latter, China, Spain, and New Zealand differ most from the others in endomorphy and mesomorphy. The numbers in all teams are small and this, combined with the large number of teams ($n = 13$), means that the Tukey test even at level $p < .05$ is rather strict; thus few significant differences were found. Despite small team numbers, differences greater than 1.0 SAD units between mean pairs are of some practical significance. There are 12 such paired differences, and 10 of these are found when comparing the Chinese and Italian means to the Spanish, Soviet, Swiss, and New Zealand teams (see Figure 4.5).

The mean somatotype for the 1977 Canadian SS (Ross et al., 1982) was $\overline{S}$ = 3.4-3.6-3.4 (SDs = 1.1, 0.9, and 1.1). These statistics are close to those in the 1991 Perth sample, with the latter being slightly less ectomorphic. The Canadian team (n = 10) in Perth had a mean of 3.1-3.3-3.2 compared to 3.4-3.3-3.3 for the 17 elite SS described by Ross et al. (1977).

Medalists Versus Others

The medalists for solo had somatotypes (rounded) of $2\frac{1}{2}$-3-$3\frac{1}{2}$, 3-3-$3\frac{1}{2}$, and 3-4-$3\frac{1}{2}$. The medalists for each pair in duet were $4\frac{1}{2}$-$4\frac{1}{2}$-2 and $3\frac{1}{2}$-5-2, $3\frac{1}{2}$-3-$3\frac{1}{2}$ and 3-4-$3\frac{1}{2}$, and $2\frac{1}{2}$-$3\frac{1}{2}$-3 and $3\frac{1}{2}$-3-3. These ratings are close to the means for Solo and Duet (see Table 4.4). The 1984 Olympic Solo and Duet gold medalists, almost identical at $3\frac{1}{2}$-$4\frac{1}{2}$-2 (Carter & Heath, 1990), were slightly more mesomorphic than all except two from the present sample.

Summary

The average somatotype (rounded) for synchronized swimmers is $3^1/_2$-$3^1/_2$-3, a central somatotype. The means for Solo, Duet, and many of the teams are also in the central category. There are no differences in somatotype as a whole by event or team, but there are some teams that differ on endomorphy and mesomorphy separately.

Water Polo

Previous Studies

There are several studies on male water polo (WP) players at the national or international level, but none on females. Leek (1968) made the earliest study on New Zealand senior and junior male players using the Parnell (1958) M.4 method of somatotyping. For the seniors (n = 77), $\overline{S}$ = 4.0-5.2-2.6, and the national team (n = 9) was almost identical with $\overline{S}$ = 4.1-5.3-2.4. Clarys and Borms (1971) somatotyped 44 Belgian water polo players using the Heath-Carter method. The means were 3.4-5.3-1.8, with 52% being endomesomorphic. At the 1968 Olympics 71 players were somatotyped (de Garay et al., 1974; Hebbelinck et al., 1975), with $\overline{S}$ = 2.9-5.3-2.3. The majority (75%) were either endomesomorphs or balanced mesomorphs, with some extreme endomesomorphs. Most of the remainder were ectomesomorphs. Rodriguez et al. (1986) reported the mean somatotype of a national Cuban team as 2.1-5.4-2.6, more ectomesomorphic than that in previous studies.

Results

Water polo players, analyzed by team place in the competition and by playing position, classfied themselves as primarily goalkeepers (GK), center backs (CB), center forwards (CF), and offensive and defensive wings—combined as "other" field players (OTH).

Males
Descriptive statistics for each team and position are given in Tables 4.6 and 4.7. The mean somatotype (rounded) for all players (n = 190) was $2^1/_2$-$5^1/_2$-$2^1/_2$, a balanced mesomorph. Ninety-one percent of the somatotypes were either endomesomorphs (33%), balanced mesomorphs (31%), or ectomesomorphs (27%). The remainder were either more ectomorphic (8%) or central (1%).

Comparisons Among Teams.
Initial comparisons among teams divided them into two groups according to final placement: places 2 through 7 and places 8 through 16 (the first-place team, Yugoslavia, was not measured). For teams 2 through 7, the means did not differ, $F(5,69)$ = 0.751, but the German team had a greater SAM than the Spanish, $F(6,69)$ = 2.175, p < .05. For teams 8 through 16 there were no differences among means, $F(8,106)$ = 1.658, or among SAMs, $F(8,106)$ = 1.940. One-way ANOVAs (df = 14,175) using the 15 teams for each component showed no differences for endomorphy, F = 1.552, but the Tukey test showed that the Greek team was more mesomorphic than the French team, even though F = 1.551, p < .10. The Greeks were also less ectomorphic, F = 1.746, p < .05 than the French. The mean somatoplots and the distribution limits are shown in Figure 4.6

Best Versus Rest.
Further analyses were made by combining the three semifinalists (Spain, Hungary, and USA) into one group and comparing them to the six teams (Greece, Cuba, France, Canada, Egypt, and New Zealand) whose means were the farthest from the semifinalist group mean. The somatotype means were significantly different, $F(6,108)$ = 2.500, p < .05. The multiple-range tests confirmed the differences between the Greek and French teams cited previously. However, the comparisons of interest were those between the semifinalists and each of the six teams. The Tukey tests were not significant, but differences of 0.6 (Cuba), 0.7 (France), and 1.3 (Greece) may be of practical interest. One-way ANOVAs for each component resulted in no siginficant differences between the semifinalists and other teams. SAMs were significantly different, $F(6,108)$ = 2.245, p < .05. The New Zealanders had a greater SAM than the semifinalists and the Egyptians.

Comparisons by Playing Position.
The SANOV analysis by position showed that there were differences between GK and CF, $F(3,186)$ = 2.686, p < .05 (see Figure 4.7). One-way ANOVAs (df = 3,186) showed that GK were more ectomorphic than CF, F = 3.519, p < .05, but there were no differences for endomorphy (F = 1.996) or mesomorphy (F = 2.472). Although the F-ratio for SAMs was significant, $F(3,186)$ = 3.196, p < .05, no pairs of differences were significant in the multiple-range tests.

Females
Descriptive statistics for each position and team are given in Tables 4.7 and 4.8. The mean somatotype (rounded) for all players (n = 109) was $3^1/_2$-4-3, borderline

Table 4.6　Somatotype Characteristics of Male Water Polo Players According to Team and Place

Team	Place	N	Component	M	SD	Low	High
Spain	2	13	Endo	2.2	0.5	1.5	3.2
			Meso	5.1	0.5	4.3	6.2
			Ecto	2.7	0.6	1.8	3.9
Hungary	3	13	Endo	2.4	0.6	1.4	3.4
			Meso	5.4	0.7	4.2	6.8
			Ecto	2.3	0.6	1.3	3.4
USA	4	11	Endo	2.5	0.7	1.4	3.8
			Meso	4.9	0.9	3.4	4.9
			Ecto	3.0	0.6	1.7	3.8
Germany	5	13	Endo	2.5	0.7	1.2	3.9
			Meso	5.1	1.3	3.4	8.0
			Ecto	2.7	1.1	0.5	4.2
Italy	6	12	Endo	2.1	0.5	1.6	3.0
			Meso	5.0	0.7	4.0	6.2
			Ecto	2.5	0.8	1.1	3.7
USSR	7	13	Endo	2.1	0.8	1.3	3.7
			Meso	5.2	1.1	3.7	7.3
			Ecto	2.5	0.8	0.9	3.8
Australia	8	13	Endo	2.9	0.8	1.7	4.0
			Meso	5.3	1.1	3.4	6.8
			Ecto	2.3	0.9	1.1	3.9
Romania	9	12	Endo	2.6	0.6	1.4	3.5
			Meso	5.1	0.4	4.6	5.8
			Ecto	2.5	0.6	1.6	3.4
Greece	10	13	Endo	2.6	1.0	1.3	4.8
			Meso	6.2	1.0	4.9	8.3
			Ecto	1.9	0.6	0.5	2.6
Cuba	11	13	Endo	2.5	0.6	1.2	3.3
			Meso	5.6	1.0	3.8	7.4
			Ecto	2.2	0.7	0.8	3.9
France	12	13	Endo	2.8	0.7	1.8	4.2
			Meso	4.8	1.1	1.9	6.3
			Ecto	3.0	1.2	1.3	6.0
Canada	13	13	Endo	2.4	0.4	1.4	2.9
			Meso	5.5	1.2	3.7	7.1
			Ecto	2.5	0.9	1.2	3.8
China	14	12	Endo	2.9	1.2	1.1	4.6
			Meso	5.3	1.0	3.8	7.2
			Ecto	2.3	1.0	1.1	4.4

Team	Place	N	Component	M	SD	Low	High
Egypt	15	13	Endo	2.3	0.6	1.6	3.5
			Meso	5.4	0.7	4.3	6.5
			Ecto	2.2	0.6	1.0	3.1
New Zealand	16	13	Endo	2.2	1.1	1.4	4.8
			Meso	5.5	1.2	3.8	7.4
			Ecto	2.3	1.1	0.8	4.3

Table 4.7 Somatotype Characteristics of Male and Female Water Polo Players According to Playing Position

Playing position	N		Somatotype	HWR[a]	SAM[b]
Male					
Goalkeeper	30	M	2.3-4.9-2.9	42.9	1.5
		SD	0.7 1.2 1.1	1.6	0.9
Center back	25	M	2.5-5.5-2.4	42.3	1.3
		SD	0.9 0.9 0.9	1.2	0.7
Center forward	40	M	2.7-5.5-2.2	42.0	1.5
		SD	0.8 1.1 0.9	1.4	0.7
Other	95	M	2.4-5.3-2.4	42.3	1.2
		SD	0.7 0.9 0.7	0.9	0.6
Total	190	M	2.5-5.3-2.4	42.4	1.3
		SD	0.8 1.0 0.9	1.2	0.7
Female					
Goalkeeper	14	M	3.6-3.5-3.2	43.5	1.0
		SD	0.9 0.6 0.7	0.7	0.5
Center back	9	M	4.1-4.0-2.5	42.5	1.3
		SD	1.1 0.7 0.9	1.3	0.7
Center forward	27	M	3.8-4.1-2.5	42.4	1.5
		SD	1.0 0.9 0.9	1.3	0.3
Other	46	M	3.5-3.9-2.9	43.0	1.2
		SD	0.9 0.8 0.8	1.1	0.6
Total	96	M	3.6-3.9-2.8	42.9	1.3
		SD	0.9 0.8 0.9	1.2	0.5

[a]HWR = height to cube root weight ratio; [b]SAM = somatotype attitudinal mean.

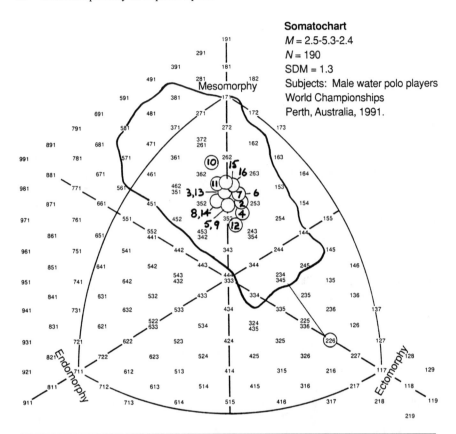

Figure 4.6   Limits of the somatotype distribution for male water polo players. Means for each team are plotted by place. Key: 2 = Spain; 3 = Hungary; 4 = USA; 5 = Germany; 6 = Italy; 7 = USSR; 8 = Australia; 9 = Romania; 10 = Greece; 11 = Cuba; 12 = France; 13 = Canada; 14 = China; 15 = Egypt; 16 = New Zealand. The circled 226 is a goalkeeper.

between the central and endomesomorphic categories. Mesomorphy is highest, with endomorphy and ectomorphy lower than one half-unit each. In general, the somatotypes for all teams are distributed along, and on either side of, the ectomorphic axis (see Figure 4.8). There are no somatotypes with ectomorphy higher than 4.7, but endomorphy ranges from $1^{1}/_{2}$ to 6, and mesomorphy from 2 to $6^{1}/_{2}$. Approximately 50% of the somatotypes are to the left of central, 30% are balanced mesomorphs or central, 15% are to the right of central, and 5% are in the lower sector, wherein mesomorphy is lower than either endomorphy or ectomorphy.

Comparisons Among Teams.

There were no differences between team means, F(8,100) = 1.24, or between SAMs, F(8,100) = 0.89. The differences in component units between mean somatotypes for the French team compared to all others (except for the Canadian

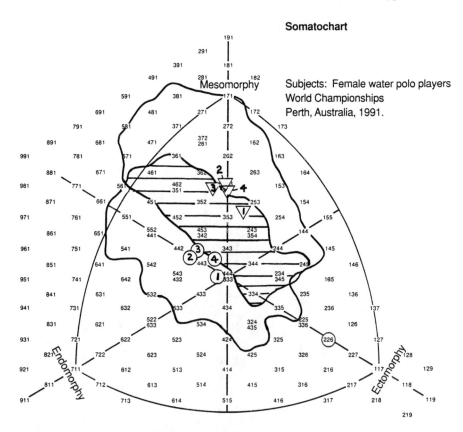

Figure 4.7   Limits of the somatotype distribution for male (upper) and female (lower) water polo players, with somatoplots of means by playing position; male means are tri-angles, and female means are circles. Key: 1 = goalkeepers; 2 = center backs; 3 = center forwards; 4 = wings (others). Hatching shows area of overlap.

and USA teams) were greater than 1.0. However, one-way ANOVAs (df = 8,100) for each component were not significant: endomorphy, F = 1.25; mesomorphy, F = 1.11; and ectomorphy, F = 0.80.

Best Versus Rest.

There were no differences between the four semifinalists and the five lower ranked teams for either somatotype means, F(1,107) = 0.30, or SAMs, F(1,107) = 0.12. The largest variations, as seen in the SAMs, are in the first (Netherlands) and the ninth (France) teams; the Hungarian and Brazilian teams have the small-est SAMs.

Comparisons by Playing Position.

Because 13 players did not identify their playing position, only 96 players were included in this analysis (see Table 4.7 and Figure 4.7). The mean somatotype

Table 4.8   Somatotype Characteristics of Female Water Polo Players According to Team and Place

Team	Place	N	Component	M	SD	Low	High
Netherlands	1	13	Endo	3.7	1.3	2.0	6.1
			Meso	3.9	1.0	2.1	6.0
			Ecto	2.9	0.9	1.1	4.4
Canada	2	11	Endo	3.4	1.0	2.3	5.3
			Meso	4.3	0.7	3.2	5.7
			Ecto	2.4	0.7	1.1	3.4
USA	3	12	Endo	3.1	1.1	2.2	6.1
			Meso	4.1	0.8	2.7	5.5
			Ecto	3.0	1.0	1.2	4.4
Hungary	4	12	Endo	3.8	1.0	2.5	6.1
			Meso	3.6	0.7	2.4	5.2
			Ecto	3.0	0.8	1.5	4.3
Australia	5	13	Endo	3.4	0.7	2.5	4.6
			Meso	3.7	0.8	2.1	4.7
			Ecto	3.0	0.9	1.4	4.7
Germany	6	8	Endo	3.9	0.9	2.2	4.9
			Meso	3.9	0.8	2.4	5.1
			Ecto	2.7	1.0	1.3	4.7
New Zealand	7	14	Endo	3.8	0.8	2.6	5.4
			Meso	3.9	0.9	2.6	5.8
			Ecto	2.6	0.9	1.0	4.0
Brazil	8	13	Endo	3.9	0.8	3.0	5.5
			Meso	3.9	0.6	3.0	5.6
			Ecto	2.7	0.9	0.9	3.8
France	9	13	Endo	3.0	1.1	1.4	4.6
			Meso	4.5	1.0	2.7	6.3
			Ecto	2.4	1.1	0.5	4.2
Total	1-9	109	Endo	3.6	1.0	1.4	6.1
			Meso	4.0	0.9	2.1	6.3
			Ecto	2.8	0.9	0.5	4.7

for all position players was 3.6-3.9-2.8, almost identical to that of the total sample (N = 109), 3.5-4.0-2.7. All four positions were similar in mean somatotype, $F(3,92) = 2.23$, and in SAMs, $F(3,92) = 1.25$, (see Figure 4.7). One-way ANOVAs by component revealed a significant difference in ectomorphy, $F(3,92) = 3.20$, $p < .027$, but the Tukey multiple-range test was not significant. The F-ratios for mesomorphy and endomorphy were 2.31 and 1.41, respectively.

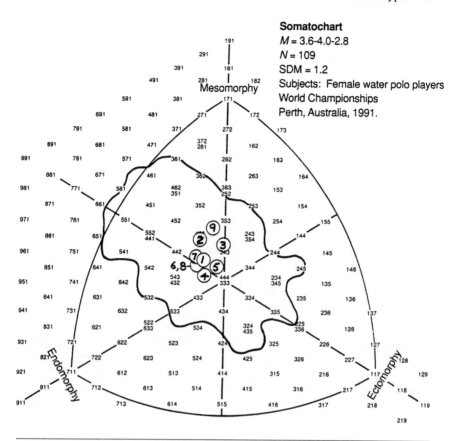

Figure 4.8 Limits of the somatotype distribution for female water polo players. Means for each team are plotted by place. Key: 1 = Netherlands; 2 = Canada; 3 = USA; 4 = Hungary; 5 = Australia; 6 = Germany; 7 = New Zealand; 8 = Brazil; 9 = France.

Discussion

Males

In general, the somatotypes of WP are clustered around the center of the somatochart's mesomorphic sector. Most of the team means are near the 2-5-2 and 3-6-3 somatoplots. Greeks, highest on the somatochart, are the most mesomorphic ($\overline{S}$ = 2.6-6.2-1.9); the lowest are the French ($\overline{S}$ = 2.8-4.8-3.0), with a mean influenced by a 2-2-6 somatotype, the most linear of all players. (Without this player the French mean would be 2.9-5.1-2.7.) The overlap among teams is considerable, partly due to variation in the different positions within teams. GK tend to be more linear than others and are significantly more so than CF. Nine players are extreme endomesomorphs (i.e., those outside the somatochart's upper left boundary), 4 being CF, and 1 GK. Out of 15 players, 8 of the most ectomorphic (southeast on the somatochart) are GK, and 2 are CF. Overall, there is considerable overlap in the three field positions.

Despite weak statistical evidence, there is an indication that the three semi-finalists are slightly less mesomorphic than some of the lower placed teams. The Greeks (10th) are clearly more mesomorphic (by 1.0 units), and the Cubans (11th), Canadians (13th), and New Zealanders (16th) are higher than the semifinalists by 0.3 to 0.4 units. The distribution of the semifinalists is slightly more restricted than several of the lower ranked teams, having no extreme endomesomorphs or dominant ectomorphs among their somatotypes.

Compared to the 1968 Olympic sample, the present sample is slightly lower in endomorphy (height-corrected in both samples), 2.5 and 2.7, but equal in mesomorphy, and is 0.1 higher in ectomorphy. The Belgian players were considerably more endomorphic (0.7, height-corrected), and less ectomorphic (–0.6) than the present sample. The 1991 New Zealand team appears much less endomorphic (–0.6) and more ectomorphic (0.6) than their 1967 counterparts (using the M.4 ratings). The 1991 Cuban team is slightly more endomesomorphic than the mid-1980s National team, 2.5-5.6-2.2 versus 2.1-5.4-2.6.

Females

There is wide variation in female WP somatotypes by both team and playing position. There was a tendency toward more linearity in GK, with 10 out of 14 somatoplots central or to the right of center; none were extreme left. Other than this observation, the distributions by position overlap considerably. The top three teams, Netherlands, Canada, and USA, did not differ noticeably from lower placed teams. Overall their means were close to other teams, with distributions at least as varied.

Summary

The average male WP somatotype is $2^1/_2$-$5^1/_2$-$2^1/_2$, a balanced mesomorph, but there are almost equal numbers slightly more endomesomorphic or ectomesomorphic. Only a few small differences between teams exist, with a tendency for more ectomorphic GK. The semifinalists, similar in somatotype to most other teams, were less mesomorphic than the Greeks (10th) and were less variable than the New Zealanders (16th).

Female WP have an average somatotype of $3^1/_2$-4-3, with the majority of somatotypes being more endomorphic than ectomorphic. There are no major differences among teams by place, or by playing position; although, like the males, there is a tendency for more ectomorphic GK.

Concluding Remarks

The somatotype characteristics of athletes in the four sports show that their distributions are much more restricted than those for nonathlete populations (Carter & Heath, 1990). In each sport there are relatively few differences by event, playing position, or performance level.

Chapter 5

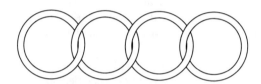

Relative Body Size

William D. Ross, Rob M. Leahy, Juan C. Mazza, and Donald T. Drinkwater

Proportion is the relative size of one part to another or to the whole of an object. Ratios are often used to indicate proportional size. However, ratios are not additive and they cannot be used in variance analyses.

Most of the objections to ratio use discussed by Packard and Boardman (1988) and Tanner (1949) are overcome by the Phantom Stratagem for proportional growth assessment introduced by Ross and Wilson (1974). Their general formula for calculating a Phantom z-score, a kind of ratio without numerator variation, uses a selected scaling constant (e.g., stature, 170.18 cm). The Phantom assessment of relative body size facilitates common-scale comparisons between one body part and any other in an individual, comparisons between individuals, or those among mean values of any group.

Previous studies on athletes in international aquatic sports, using similar relative body size or proportionality approaches to those in this chapter, have been reported by Hebbelinck et al. (1975) for Olympic swimmers, divers, and water polo players; by Perez (1981) for Venezualan swimmers; by Ross, Ward, Leahy, and Day (1982) for Olympic swimmers; and by Mazza et al. (1991b) for

Note. We wish to acknowledge support from the Canadian Fitness and Lifestyle Research Institute.

South American swimmers. This chapter compares athletes in swimming, diving, synchronized swimming, and water polo to determine proportionality characteristics associated with each sport, by event, playing position, or performance level.

Methods

Phantom z-values were calculated for 34 of the anthropometric dimensions obtained on the 919 athletes in KASP. The Phantom specifications (i.e., P and S values) for use in the following general equation are given in Ross, De Rose, and Ward (1988) and Ross and Marfell-Jones (1991). In the equation

$$z = 1/S \ (V \ (170.18 \ / \ h)^d - P),$$

z is a proportionality score, or z-value; S is the Phantom standard deviation for a variable (V); V is any given length, breadth, girth, skinfold thickness, or other obtained measure for the Phantom-specified variable; 170.18 is the constant for Phantom stature; h is the subject's stature; d is a dimensional exponent for the geometrical similarity system where d = 1 for all lengths, d = 2 for all areas, d = 3 for all masses; and P is the Phantom-specified size for a variable (V).

The KASP data were arranged in spreadsheet form to facilitate analyses. Selection of categories, calculation of z-values, and generation of proportionality profiles and summary tables were all done within the context of this spreadsheet.

An inspectional test determined differences between groups. If the standard error bars about a sample mean did not overlap those of another mean, differences were deemed significant (Ross et al., 1982). Two factors that ascertain a difference between means and are key therefore in ascribing positive and negative signs are the size of the difference and the size of the standard errors for each sample $(SD/n^{0.5})$. For this reason, some relatively large z-value differences as plotted in the figures may not be significant, whereas some relatively smaller differences may be. (Note: this approach is very liberal and will tend to exaggerate Type I errors when several comparisons are involved.)

Because of space limitations, graphs showing standard error bars are not presented. Instead, results of these comparisons are shown in summary tables. If the difference between sample means was greater than or equal to the sum of the standard errors about the samples, the difference was displayed as positive (+); if the difference was negative, this was displayed as negative (−). If there was no difference, no entry was displayed.

Summarizing the multiple comparisons, we arranged variables in tables showing proportionality for each group comparison. Variables from left to right are: proportional body mass (Prop M), arm span, sitting height, (and then in four groups) 6 lengths, 6 breadths, 11 girths, and 8 skinfolds. These last four groups are generally viewed as characteristics from least to most influenced by training and nutrition.

The first three variables give an overall impression of proportional structure; proportional mass (#1) has a perfect inverse relationship with the subject's ponderosity or ectomorphy rating; arm span (#2) and sitting height (#3) indicate segmental lengths and breadths. Lengths (#4 - #9) and breadths (#10 - #15) reflect the relative skeletal dimensions of the body. Girths (#16 - #26) (apart from head, wrist, and ankle) enable one to appraise the relative contribution of muscularity to proportional body mass, especially in the limbs, as well as to appreciate the regional pattern of girths. In other than athletic samples, skinfold-corrected girths give a better indication of the underlying musculature than the uncorrected girths. Skinfold-corrected girths were not included in this analysis. The relative adiposity of an individual or group can be appraised by the proportional skinfold thickness at eight sites, or in regional groupings for the upper extremities (#27, #29), torso (#28, #30-#32), and lower extremities (#33, #34).

Reference Groups

Comparisons by event groups and Best versus Rest (see Table 5.1) were made using selected reference groups as the zero line for the graph displays and show direction of proportional differences by variable. Using this procedure results in some comparisons in this chapter that are different from those in other chapters. However, they are similar enough in most instances to make possible cross-chapter group comparisons.

Swimming

Previous Studies

Ross et al. (1982) reported proportional differences for 33 male swimmers compared to 32 female swimmers measured at the 1976 Montreal Olympic Games. The only differences by event were seen in proportional body mass. Based on the graphs presented, both male and female 200 m butterfly swimmers, were proportionally the heaviest, with proportional body masses of about 66 kg and 67 kg, respectively. For the males, 200 m freestyle and 100 m and 200 m backstroke swimmers were proportionally the lightest, about 56 kg. For the females, the 400 m and 800 m freestyle swimmers were proportionally the lightest, about 58 kg. Hebbelinck et al. (1975) reported that male individual medley swimmers compared to other styles were relatively broader in skeletal measures, lowest in skinfolds, and, like breaststrokers, were larger in arm and calf girths. In females, individual medley and breaststroke swimmers were relatively larger in biacromial breadth, chest depth, and arm girth. Analyses by event were not made in other studies.

Results

Male and female 50 + 100 m FR sprinters were the designated reference groups against which the other event groups were compared (see Table 5.1).

Male Swimmers

The proportionality characteristics of swimmers in seven events were compared to those of the 50 + 100 m FR, as summarized in Table 5.2.

Table 5.1   Reference and Comparison Groups for Proportionality Assessment

Sport	Reference group	Comparison groups
Swimming Male and female	50 + 100 m free	50 + 100 m BR 50 + 100 m BK 50 + 100 m FL 200 + 400 m FR 200 m IM 400 m IM 800 m FR (female) 1500 m FR (male) 25 km LD
	50 + 100 m BR 50 + 100 m BK 50 + 100 m FL	200 m BR 200 m BK 200-m FL
Male and female, for above 12 comparisons:	rank > 12 (Rest)	rank ≤ 12 (Best)
Diving Male and female	1M 10M rank > 10 (Rest)	3M rank ≤ 10 (Best)
Synchronized swimming	Team Team rank > 4 (Rest)	Duet Solo Team rank ≤ 4 (Best)
Water polo	Other (wings) Female teams > 4th (Rest) Male teams > 4th (Rest)	Center forward Goalkeeper Center back Teams 1 to 4 Teams 2 to 4

Compared to 50 + 100 m FR, the 50 + 100 m BR were proportionally heavier, longer in sitting height and foot length, larger in biacromial breadth and AP chest depth, and had larger forearm, wrist, hip, and thigh girths. The 50 + 100 m BK were longer in sitting height, shorter in forearm length, and larger in femur breadth and calf girth. Compared to reference sprinters, 50 + 100 m FL were the most distinctive, being proportionally heavier, with greater span, longer forearm, and shorter thigh lengths—much more robust than reference swimmers. Apart from transverse chest and humerus breadths, head girth, iliac crest, and medial calf skinfolds, they were proportionally larger than 50 + 100 m FR in all other breadths, girths, and skinfolds (see Table 5.2).

The 200 IM were larger in arm and foot length, and hip, thigh, and ankle girths. The 400 IM were smaller in arm and leg length and larger in sitting height,

Table 5.2 Proportionality Differences in Male Swimmers by Event and Performance

	1 Prop M	2 Span	3 Sitting H	4 Arm L	5 Forearm L	6 Hand L	7 Thigh L	8 Leg L	9 Foot L	10 Biacromial B	11 Tr Chest B	12 AP Chest B	13 Biiliocristal B	14 Humerus B	15 Femur B	16 Head G	17 Neck G	18 Arm G	19 Forearm G	20 Wrist G	21 Chest G	22 Waist G	23 Hip G	24 Thigh G	25 Calf G	26 Ankle G	27 Triceps SF	28 Subscapular SF	29 Biceps SF	30 Iliac crest SF	31 Supraspinale SF	32 Abdominal SF	33 Front thigh SF	34 Medial calf SF
Male swimming																																		
Male 50 and 100 m in BR, BK, and FL compared to 50 + 100 m sprint FR																																		
50 + 100 BR	+		+						+	+		+							+			+	+	+										
50 + 100 BK			+		–									+											+									
50 + 100 FL	+	+		+			–		+	+		+		+		+	+	+	+	+	+	+	+	+	+	+	+	+		+	+	+	+	
Male 200 m IM, 400 m IM, 1500 m FR & LD compared to 50 + 100 m FR																																		
200 IM				+				+														+	+		+									
400 IM	+		–				–				+				+				+								+	+						

(continued)

Table 5.2 *(continued)*

	1 Prop M	2 Span	3 Sitting H	4 Arm L	5 Forearm L	6 Hand L	7 Thigh L	8 Leg L	9 Foot L	10 Biacromial B	11 Tr Chest B	12 AP Chest B	13 Biiliocristal B	14 Humerus B	15 Femur B	16 Head G	17 Neck G	18 Arm G	19 Forearm G	20 Wrist G	21 Chest G	22 Waist G	23 Hip G	24 Thigh G	25 Calf G	26 Ankle G	27 Triceps SF	28 Subscapular SF	29 Biceps SF	30 Iliac crest SF	31 Supraspinale SF	32 Abdominal SF	33 Front thigh SF	34 Medial calf SF
1500 FR	+			+													−	−				+		−		+		−				−		
LD	+				+						+	+	+	+	+	+	+	+	+	+	+	+	+	+	+	+	+	+	+	+	+	+	+	+
200 + 400 FR						−								−								+					+		+	+	+	+	+	+
200 BR	+						+		+			+		+	+					+	+	+				+			+					
200 BK	−		−									−			−			−	−		−	−	−	−	−				+					
200 FL						−										+																		

Male 200 m and 400 m compared to 50 + 100 m sprinters in the same stroke

Males in first 12 places in their preferred event (Best) compared to nonplacers (Rest)

50 + 100 BR	+		+		−	+			−	−
50 + 100 BK		+	+	+		+			−	−
50 + 100 FL	−	−	−		−		−	−	−	
200 + 400 FR			+	−	−	−		−		
200 BR	−	+	−	−	−	−				
200 BK	+		+	+	+					
200 FL	−			−			−			
200 IM		−	+			−	+	−		
400 IM					−			+		
1500 FR			+					−		
LD	−		−	−						

Note. The compared groups are listed above each section. The + and − signs show the direction of the significant differences.

biacromial breadth, AP chest depth, head and wrist girths, and triceps and biceps skinfolds (see Table 5.2).

In the long-distance events (1500 FR and the 25 km swim or LD), LD differed most from the 50 + 100 FR sprinters, having larger proportional weight and longer forearms. Apart from biacromial breadth, they were larger in all other breadths, in all girths, and in skinfold thicknesses (see Table 5.2).

Comparison of MD with sprint swimmers in the same stroke showed different patterns. The 200 + 400 m FR, compared to 50 + 100 m FR, were smaller in hand length and humerus breadth and were larger in waist girth and all skinfolds except at the subscapular site. The 200 m BR were proportionally heavier than their 50 + 100 m BR counterparts and shorter in sitting height; but they had longer thigh and foot lengths, larger AP chest depth, humerus and femur breadths, wrist, chest, and waist girths and were larger in five of the six skinfolds. The 200 m BK were proportionally lighter than the 50 + 100 m BK sprinters and were shorter in sitting height. They were smaller in AP chest depth and femur breadths and smaller in 7 of the 11 girths. There were no discernible differences in skinfold thicknesses except for a larger biceps skinfold. The 200 m FL were similar to the 50 + 100 m FL except for a smaller forearm length and larger head girth.

There were no clear patterns of differences between the Best versus Rest except for smaller skinfolds by the Best sprint swimmers and larger upper limb girths in 200 m BK.

Female Swimmers

The most striking female characteristic is the occasional proportionally larger head size. The mean head girth (#16) in the overall KASP sample was identical to the Phantom head girth specification of 56.0 cm. The large positive z-values for head girth in some of the figures is not an artifact but reflects the proprotionally larger value obtained when persons shorter than the specified stature for the unisex Phantom are geometrically scaled to the Phantom stature (see Table 5.3).

Compared to their same-sex 50 + 100 m FR reference group, the 50 + 100 m BR were larger in foot length, humerus breadth, and ankle girth and smaller in transverse chest breadth. The 50 + 100 m BK had smaller proportional weight than the reference group. They were larger in thigh length and smaller in neck, arm, forearm, chest, and waist girths, AP chest depth, and subscapular skinfold. The 50 + 100 m FL had a larger sitting height and smaller span, forearm, thigh, and leg length, and larger biacromial breadth and head girth. Clearly, the markedly greater robustness of male FL compared to their same-sex sprint controls was not in evidence for female FL. The Best 50 + 100 m FL were smaller than the Rest of the female FL in six of the eight skinfolds.

In comparisons of the 200 + 400 m FR, the 800 m FR, and the 25 km LD, only female LD (like the males) were proportionally much heavier than the 50 + 100 m FR. They had longer sitting height and larger values in four of six breadths and in all the girths and skinfold thicknesses. Interestingly, the four best LD, compared to six others, had smaller proportional weight and were

Table 5.3 Proportionality Differences in Female Swimmers by Event and Performance

	1 Prop M	2 Span	3 Sitting H	4 Arm L	5 Forearm L	6 Hand L	7 Thigh L	8 Leg L	9 Foot L	10 Biacromial B	11 Tr Chest B	12 AP Chest B	13 Biiliocristal B	14 Humerus B	15 Femur B	16 Head G	17 Neck G	18 Arm G	19 Forearm G	20 Wrist G	21 Chest G	22 Waist G	23 Hip G	24 Thigh G	25 Calf G	26 Ankle G	27 Triceps SF	28 Subscapular SF	29 Biceps SF	30 Iliac crest SF	31 Supraspinale SF	32 Abdominal SF	33 Front thigh SF	34 Medial calf SF
Female swimming																																		
Female 50 m and 100 m in BR, BK, and FL compared to 50 + 100 m sprint FR																																		
50 + 100 BR									+					+												+								
50 + 100 BK	−						+				−	−					−	−			−	−						−						
50 + 100 FL				−	+	−	−	−		+		−				+																	+	
Female 200 m IM, 400 m IM, 800 m FR, and LD compared to 50 + 100 m FR																																		
200 IM	+							−																				−		−				
400 IM	+			+		+										+																+		

(continued)

Table 5.3 (continued)

	1 Prop M	2 Span	3 Sitting H	4 Arm L	5 Forearm L	6 Hand L	7 Thigh L	8 Leg L	9 Foot L	10 Biacromial B	11 Tr Chest B	12 AP Chest B	13 Biiliocristal B	14 Humerus B	15 Femur B	16 Head G	17 Neck G	18 Arm G	19 Forearm G	20 Wrist G	21 Chest G	22 Waist G	23 Hip G	24 Thigh G	25 Calf G	26 Ankle G	27 Triceps SF	28 Subscapular SF	29 Biceps SF	30 Iliac crest SF	31 Supraspinale SF	32 Abdominal SF	33 Front thigh SF	34 Medial calf SF
800 FR	+																								+	+	−	−		−	−	−		
LD FR			+								+	+	+	+		+	+	+	+	+	+	+	+	+	+	+	+	+	+	+	+	+	+	+
200 + 400 FR														+		+					−					+			+					+
200 BR													+			+				+					+		+							
200 BK	+						−															+												
200 FL								+	+			+			+								+			+	+						+	+

Female 200 m and 400 m compared to 50 + 100 m in the same stroke

Females in first 12 places in their preferred event (Best) compared to nonplacers (Rest)

50 + 100 BR

50 + 100 BK

50 + 100 FL

200 FR

200 BR

200 BK

200 FL

200 IM

400 IM

800 m FR 5 best of 6

LD

Note. The compared groups are listed above each section. The + and – signs show the direction of the significant differences.

smaller in 19 of the other 33 comparisons. The 800 m FR only differed from the 50 + 100 m FR in larger calf and ankle girths and lower skinfolds at five of the eight sites.

Proportional differences of female MD to female sprint swimmers in the same stroke show that 200 + 400 m FR had larger humerus breadth, smaller chest girth, and larger ankle girth, biceps, and medial calf skinfolds. The 200 m BR were larger in biiliocristal breadth, head, forearm, and calf girth, and triceps skinfold. The 200 m BK were proportionally heavier than the sprinters but differed only in a smaller thigh length and larger waist girth. The 200 m FL were larger in leg and foot length, AP chest depth, femur breadth, hip girth, ankle girth, and triceps, front thigh, and medial calf skinfolds.

Compared to same-sex 50 + 100 m FR, the 200 m IM and 400 m IM differed in that male 200 m IM were larger in arm and foot length, hip, thigh, and calf girth; female 200 m IM had longer sitting height and were shorter in leg length and smaller in subscapular and iliac crest skinfolds. Female 400 m IM had longer sitting height and hand length and larger head girth, biceps, and abdominal skinfolds.

Diving

Previous Studies

Hebbelinck et al. (1975) noted that Olympic male divers, when compared to Phantom values, were relatively large in biacromial breadth, chest depth, and arm girth, but smaller in biiliocristal breadth and thigh girth. Female divers differed little from the Phantom values.

Results

Divers who listed 1M as their primary event were used as the reference group against which the 3M and platform or 10M events were compared.

For males, there were few proportional differences. As shown in Table 5.4, the 3M divers had shorter hand and foot lengths than the 1M divers. The 10M divers had smaller transverse and AP chest dimensions, smaller forearm, chest, hip, and thigh girths, and larger triceps, biceps, and front-thigh skinfolds.

As shown in Table 5.4, female 3M and 10M divers had longer thigh and leg lengths and smaller forearm girths than the 1M divers. The 3M divers were also longer in forearm length and smaller in wrist girth. In addition, the 10M divers were proportionally smaller than 1M divers in body mass and sitting height, biacromial and chest breadths, 8 out of 11 girths, triceps, and subscapular skinfolds.

A comparison of divers placing in the top 10 (Best) with the Rest is shown in Table 5.4. The Best male divers had wider biacromial breadth, shorter forearm and leg lengths, and longer arm and thigh lengths. Thus, they were larger in proximal and smaller in distal segments than the Rest of the male divers. The Best female divers tended to be proportionally smaller than the rest of the

Table 5.4 Proportionality Differences in Male and Female Divers by Event and Performance

	Prop M	Span	Sitting H	Arm L	Forearm L	Hand L	Thigh L	Leg L	Foot L	Biacromial B	Tr Chest B	AP Chest B	Biiliocristal B	Humerus B	Femur B	Head G	Neck G	Arm G	Forearm G	Wrist G	Chest G	Waist G	Hip G	Thigh G	Calf G	Ankle G	Triceps SF	Subscapular SF	Biceps SF	Iliac crest SF	Supraspinale SF	Abdominal SF	Front thigh SF	Medial calf SF
	1	2	3	4	5	6	7	8	9	10	11	12	13	14	15	16	17	18	19	20	21	22	23	24	25	26	27	28	29	30	31	32	33	34
Diving																																		
Male 3M and 10M compared to 1M																																		
3M-1M						−																												
10 M-1M												−							−					−			+		+				+	
Females 3M and 10M compared to 1M																																		
3M-1M					+		+	+										−	−	−														
10M-1M	−		−				+	+			−							−	−		−		−	−	−	−	−	−						

(continued)

Table 5.4 (continued)

Best 10 placing in preferred 1M, 3M, 10M event (Best) compared to nonplacers (Rest)

	1 Prop M	2 Span	3 Sitting H	4 Arm L	5 Forearm L	6 Hand L	7 Thigh L	8 Leg L	9 Foot L	10 Biacromial B	11 Tr Chest B	12 AP Chest B	13 Biiliocristal B	14 Humerus B	15 Femur B	16 Head G	17 Neck G	18 Arm G	19 Forearm G	20 Wrist G	21 Chest G	22 Waist G	23 Hip G	24 Thigh G	25 Calf G	26 Ankle G	27 Triceps SF	28 Subscapular SF	29 Biceps SF	30 Iliac crest SF	31 Supraspinale SF	32 Abdominal SF	33 Front thigh SF	34 Medial calf SF
M Best-Rest				+	–		+	–		+																–		–						
F Best-Rest		–	+		–			–				–	–			–					–		–	–									–	–

Note. The compared groups are listed above each section. The + and – signs show the direction of the significant differences.

divers. They were proportionally lighter, but had longer sitting height, sometimes reflecting greater ponderosity. This was not evidenced in our data, however, as measurements were smaller in span, leg length, AP chest, and biiliocristal breadths, head, chest, hip, and thigh girths, and front thigh and medial calf skinfolds.

Synchronized Swimming

Previous Studies

Prior to KASP, there were no data available on the proportionality characteristics of synchronized swimmers.

Results

For comparison, SS were grouped into solo, duet, and team events. Ninety-four team SS served as the reference group, and comparisons are summarized in Table 5.5.

Compared to team SS, duet swimmers had proportionally longer forearms, larger AP chest depth and biiliocristal breadths, smaller wrist girth, and larger biceps skinfold. Characteristically more linear than the team swimmers, soloists were proportionally lighter, had shorter sitting height, longer arm, thigh, and foot lengths, and smaller transverse chest and femur breadths, smaller head, neck, forearm, wrist, chest, waist, hip, thigh, and ankle girths and were smaller in all skinfolds except at the supraspinale, abdominal, and front thigh sites. Comparing the top four teams with lower placed teams, the Best teams had proportionally longer spans, smaller forearm and thigh lengths, longer foot lengths, and wider biacromial and biiliocristal breadths. They also had smaller wrist and ankle girths and were smaller in all skinfolds except at the iliac crest site.

Water Polo

Previous Studies

Water polo players at the 1968 Olympics, when compared to the Phantom values, were proportionally heavier and had larger biacromial breadth, chest depth, and arm girth, but smaller biiliocristal breadth and thigh girth (Hebbelinck et al., 1975).

Results

WP were divided according to playing position (GK, CB, CF, and OTH, who were mostly offensive or defensive wings). Ninety-five male players and 59 female players listed as OTH served as the reference groups for comparisons summarized in Table 5.6.

As shown in Table 5.6, male CF were proportionally heavier than OTH, had larger span and leg length, smaller head girth (because they were taller than OTH), larger waist girth, and larger skinfolds except at the front thigh and medial

Table 5.5 Proportionality Differences in Synchronized Swimmers by Event and Performance

	1 Prop M	2 Span	3 Siting H	4 Arm L	5 Forearm L	6 Hand L	7 Thigh L	8 Leg L	9 Foot L	10 Biacromial B	11 Tr Chest B	12 AP Chest B	13 Biiliocristal B	14 Humerus B	15 Femur B	16 Head G	17 Neck G	18 Arm G	19 Forearm G	20 Wrist G	21 Chest G	22 Waist G	23 Hip G	24 Thigh G	25 Calf G	26 Ankle G	27 Triceps SF	28 Subscapular SF	29 Biceps SF	30 Iliac crest SF	31 Supraspinale SF	32 Abdominal SF	33 Front thigh SF	34 Medial calf SF
Synchronized swimming																																		
Duet and solo compared to team synchronized swimmers																																		
Duet team				+	+							+	+							−									+					
Solo team	−			+			+		+		−				−	−	−		−		−	−	−	−		−	−	−	−	−				−
Synchronized swimming teams placing in top four (Best) compared to nonplacing teams (Rest)																																		
Team Best-Rest	+		−	−			−		+	+			+							−							−	−	−	−	−	−	−	−

Note. The compared groups are listed above each section. The + and − signs show the direction of the significant differences.

Table 5.6 Proportionality Differences in Male and Female Water Polo Players by Playing Position and Performance

	1 Prop M	2 Span	3 Sitting H	4 Arm L	5 Forearm L	6 Hand L	7 Thigh L	8 Leg L	9 Foot L	10 Biacromial B	11 Tr Chest B	12 AP Chest B	13 Biiliocristal B	14 Humerus B	15 Femur B	16 Head G	17 Neck G	18 Arm G	19 Forearm G	20 Wrist G	21 Chest G	22 Waist G	23 Hip G	24 Thigh G	25 Calf G	26 Ankle G	27 Triceps SF	28 Subscapular SF	29 Biceps SF	30 Iliac crest SF	31 Supraspinale SF	32 Abdominal SF	33 Front thigh SF	34 Medial calf SF
Water polo																																		
Male CF, GK, and CB compared to OTH																																		
CF	+	+						+														+					+	+	+	+	+	+		
GK	−		−				+	+	−	−	−					−	−	−	−	−	−	+												
CB								+					+			−																+		
Female CF, GK, and CB compared to OTH																																		
CF	+						+			+	+	+	+									+		+				+		+	+	+		+

(continued)

Table 5.6 (continued)

	1 Prop M	2 Span	3 Sitting H	4 Arm L	5 Forearm L	6 Hand L	7 Thigh L	8 Leg L	9 Foot L	10 Biacromial B	11 Tr Chest B	12 AP Chest B	13 Billiocristal B	14 Humerus B	15 Femur B	16 Head G	17 Neck G	18 Arm G	19 Forearm G	20 Wrist G	21 Chest G	22 Waist G	23 Hip G	24 Thigh G	25 Calf G	26 Ankle G	27 Triceps SF	28 Subscapular SF	29 Biceps SF	30 Iliac crest SF	31 Supraspinale SF	32 Abdominal SF	33 Front thigh SF	34 Medial calf SF
GK	−		−			−	+	+	−	−	−	−		−	−	−	−	−	−	−	−	−												
CB			−		+		+	+	−	−	+				−	−	−		−	−	+					−	+	+		−	+	+	−	
M Best-Rest	−		−				+		−	−					−				−			−	−	−						−	−			
F Best-Rest					−										−	−							−	−									−	−

Male and female water polo teams placing in top four (Best) compared to nonplacing teams (Rest)

Note. The compared groups are listed above each section. The + and − signs show the direction of the significant differences.

calf sites. Compared to OTH, GK were proportionally lighter and had shorter sitting height, longer thigh length, smaller biacromial and transverse chest depth, and smaller head, neck, arm, forearm, chest, and waist girths. CB were similar to OTH except for longer leg and smaller foot length, wider biacromial breadth, smaller head girth, and larger abdominal skinfold.

Table 5.6 indicates that female WP show patterns similar to the males. CF were proportionally heavier than OTH, with larger thigh length, biacromial, AP chest depth and biiliocristal breadth, waist and thigh girths, and larger skinfolds at subscapular, iliac crest, supraspinale, abdominal, and medial calf sites. GK had smaller proportional weight than OTH, shorter sitting height, and longer thigh and leg length, but smaller hand and foot lengths. They were smaller in all except biiliocristal breadth and all upper body girths except waist girth. They did not differ in lower body girths or skinfold thicknesses.

The second- to fourth-place male teams and the first- to fourth-place female teams were compared with their same-sex OTH reference group. The Best WP teams of both sexes tended to be proportionally smaller than the Rest. Males were proportionally lighter, shorter in sitting height, larger in thigh length, and smaller in hand and foot length. They were smaller in biacromial and femur breadths, and forearm, wrist, waist, hip, and thigh girths, and in iliac crest and supraspinale skinfolds. Compared to the Rest, the Best female WP had smaller arm span, forearm length, femur breadth, head, hip, and thigh girths, and front thigh and medial calf skinfolds.

Concluding Remarks

In all sports there were proportionality differences between athletes by event, playing position, or performance level. Differences in absolute size were not entirely eliminated by individual scaling from a wide range of stature to the Phantom-specified stature. The present findings are not strictly comparable to previous studies, which used smaller numbers, some different variables, and different criteria for event grouping.

In swimming there were differences by event and distance, with male and female LD being proportionally larger than other FR. Male FL were more robust than those in other strokes, but this was not true for females. The 10M divers of both sexes tended to be proportionally smaller than 1M divers; 3M divers were somewhat intermediate in proportional size. Solo SS were more linear than team swimmers, with duet swimmers less so. In WP there were some differences by playing position, with CF proportionally larger than GK and OTH. The Best teams were proportionally smaller for several variables than the Rest.

These generalized findings suggest that there may be underlying biomechanical reasons for these differences, which in turn affect technique. However, the patterns of differences in some sports were not consistent or clear. Further study and analyses are needed to clarify their meaning and importance. At present it appears that although there are physique requirements within the four aquatic sports, they are not unduly restrictive with regard to proportionality.

Chapter 6

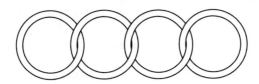

Body Composition

Donald T. Drinkwater and Juan C. Mazza

Several approaches have been presented herein characterizing the structure and shape of athletes participating in diving, swimming, synchronized swimming, and water polo at the 1991 World Championships in Perth, Australia. Descriptive statistics for each anthropometric item are presented by gender, sport, and event in chapter 3. The somatotype analyses in chapter 4 evaluate the athletes according to shape and composition characterized in terms of endomorphy, mesomorphy, and ectomorphy. Chapter 5 addresses body shape by using clusters of body dimensions to examine proportional differences in the various sports groups. A fourth approach, presented in this chapter evaluates the body composition of these athletes in terms of fatness (adiposity), muscularity, and skeletal structure.

Previous studies of athletes, summarized by Carter (1982a, 1984a), have considered body composition, focusing on the evaluation of relative body fatness and its impact on performance. It is rarely possible during large-scale surveys to assess body composition by conventional laboratory methods such as hydro-densitometry; therefore, much of the information on body composition of elite athletes has been inferred from anthropometry.

Various skinfold measurements have been used in comparison with adipose tissue patterning among participants in different sports. The sums of skinfolds have also been used as indicators of adiposity or relative body fatness. In keeping with previous studies on Olympic athletes (Carter et al., 1982b; Carter & Yuhasz, 1984) the sum of six skinfolds (SUM6SF) is used in this study to indicate body fatness. Athletes with a high SUM6SF are considered fatter than those with a smaller value.

In addition to fatness, evaluation of the musculoskeletal compartment may be equally important to assess performance or to determine potential for performance. Aside from the advantages or disadvantages of absolute size in some sports, the extent to which an athlete is successful in many sports may depend on the amount of muscle relative to body mass and, to a degree, on the amount of muscle relative to skeletal mass.

Carter and Yuhasz (1984) evaluated the body composition of Olympic athletes in various sports and suggested that, unlike sports where excess fat is a disadvantage, in sports such as long-distance swimming, water polo, and synchronized swimming, moderate fat levels might be advantageous for providing positive buoyancy. Elite swimmers in events other than long-distance swimming exhibit body fat levels comparable to other highly trained athletes. Perhaps, then, a more important consideration is the impact of a high skeletal mass relative to muscle or to fat on body density and buoyancy and the subsequent effect these variables might have on performance.

To evaluate muscularity and skeletal structure, we made estimates of total body muscle mass and total body skeletal mass using formulae derived from the cadaver studies described by Clarys, Martin, and Drinkwater (1984). Note that, like anthropometrically derived body fat estimates, these are also derived from anthropometry and subject to the same limitations. Furthermore, these tissue masses represent those of functional tissues in an anatomical rather than chemical partitioning of the body. Hence, the summation of muscle and skeletal mass *does not* represent, neither is it equivalent to, fat-free mass or lean body mass.

Methods

The six skinfolds sum (SUM6SF) used as an indicator of body fatness were: triceps + subscapular + abdominal + supraspinale + front thigh + medial calf skinfolds. No correction was made for stature. Muscle mass was calculated according to Martin, Spenst, Drinkwater, and Clarys (1990). Although this equation was based on male cadaver data, we made no differentiation in muscle mass calculations for males or females in this study. The equation for calculating muscle mass was

$$\text{Estimated muscle mass (kg)} = (\text{STAT} \times (0.0553 \times \text{CMTG}^2 + 0.0987 \times \text{FG}^2 + 0.0331 \times \text{CCG}^2) - 2445) / 1000$$

where STAT is stature (cm); CMTG is midthigh girth (cm) corrected for front thigh skinfold thickness (FTSF, mm); CMTG = MTG − Pi × FTSF / 10; Pi =

3.1416; FG is uncorrected forearm girth; CCG is calf girth (cm) corrected for medial calf skinfold thickness (MCSF, mm); CCG = CG − Pi × MCSF / 10.

Martin et al. (1990) have reported a correlation coefficient of 0.98 and a standard error of estimate of 1.53 kg for this regression. Percent muscle mass was calculated as estimated muscle mass divided by body mass times 100.

Skeletal mass was calculated according to Martin (1991) using an equation derived from data of older adult male and female cadavers. We made no differentiation in skeletal mass calculations for males or females in this study. The equation for calculating skeletal mass was

$$\text{Estimated skeletal mass (kg)} = 0.00006 \times \text{STAT} \times$$
$$(\text{FEMRB} + \text{HUMRB} + \text{WRSTB} + \text{ANKLB})^2$$

where STAT is stature (cm); FEMRB is femur breadth (cm); HUMRB is humerus breadth (cm); WRSTB is wrist breadth (cm); ANKLB is ankle breadth (cm). The standard error of estimate for this equation was given as 0.95% of predicted skeletal mass; no correlation coefficient was given. Percent skeletal mass was calculated as estimated skeletal mass divided by body mass times 100.

Note that, because ankle girth (not ankle breadth) was measured in this study, ankle breadth was estimated using the following equation:

$$\text{Ankle breadth} = 1.035 + 0.875 \times \text{Ankle girth}.$$

This equation was determined from anthropometric data on 151 adults (72 males, 79 females) age 18 to 70 yr (unpublished data) and has a correlation coefficient of 0.75. The standard error of estimate (0.37 cm) was approximately the same technical error of measurement as that for ankle breadth.

Anthropometry cannot be used in assessment of bone mineral density (BMD); therefore, certain assumptions about skeletal density must be made. Male BMD is greater than female BMD (Lohman, Slaughter, Boileau, Bunt, & Lussier, 1984). Thus, if an average male or female skeletal density is assumed, anthropometric skeletal mass will be overestimated in females and underestimated in males. A further difficulty is that the equation is based on the Brussels Cadaver Study whose older subjects would have lost bone mineral in their skeletal mass. Thus, young adult skeletal mass would likely be underestimated. However, in the context of this study, skeletal mass might not be appreciably underestimated, because there are reports of lower BMD in swimmers relative to athletes in other sports (Heinrich, Going, Pamenter, Boyden, & Lohman, 1990; Risser, Lee, LeBlanc, Poindexter, Risser, & Schneider, 1990). Muscle mass divided by skeletal mass was calculated to provide the muscle to skeletal mass ratio.

For convenience, chapter tables present stature and body mass together with SUM6SF, percent muscle mass, percent skeletal mass, and muscle:skeletal–mass ratio. Stature and body mass data permit the calculation of muscle and skeletal masses and suggest the degree of dependence that relative tissue masses have on stature.

As in previous chapters, this chapter has no comparisons across sports or by gender, but rather by event and gender within each sport. Analysis of variance procedures (ANOVA) and Tukey range testing (SPSS Inc., 1991) were used for all comparisons. The level of significance was set at $p < .05$.

Swimming

Previous Studies

As reported in preceding chapters, several studies have examined swimmers at the national and international level. Few studies, however, have provided information about body composition. Carter and Yuhasz (1984) reported the average SUM6SF and skinfold patterns for male and female Olympic swimmers. For 33 males (body mass = 73.0 kg) measured at the 1976 Montreal Olympics, the average SUM6SF was 47.2 mm. For 32 females (body mass = 57.8 kg) the average SUM6SF was 76.9 mm. For 14 males (body mass = 74.9 kg) and 7 females (body mass = 60.1 kg) measured in Munich, 1972, by Novak et al., (1976a, 1976b), the average SUM6SF was 55.0 mm and 71.2 mm, respectively. The Munich study used the iliac crest skinfold in place of the supraspinale skinfold, which would result in a SUM6SF number 4 to 6 mm higher than with a supraspinale skinfold. In 1968 at the Mexico City Olympics, 65 male swimmers (body mass = 72.1 kg) had a sum of four skinfolds (SUM4) of 28.2 mm compared to 28.7 mm for swimmers at Montreal (body mass = 73.0 kg). In addition, 27 female swimmers at Mexico City (body mass = 57.4 kg) had a SUM4 of 43.9 mm compared to 44.6 mm for 32 swimmers at Montreal (body mass = 57.8 kg). Thus the comparisons between these Olympics by gender are quite similar for body mass and skinfold totals.

Results and Discussion

For analysis, swimmers were separated by gender and by primary stroke and distance. Descriptive statistics by stroke and distance are shown in Table 6.1 and 6.2 (males) and 6.3 and 6.4 (females).

For all 231 male swimmers the average SUM6SF was 45.8 mm, a value similar to that of 47.2 mm for the Montreal swimmers measured in 1976 (Carter et al., 1982b). For the 170 female swimmers the average SUM6SF was 72.6 mm, a value marginally lower (−4.3 mm) than that of 76.9 mm reported by Carter et al. Thus, these data are consistent with previous studies.

Comparisons Between Strokes

Initial event groups consisted of four freestyle (FR), two each in breaststroke (BR), backstroke (BK), and butterfly (FL), one for individual medley (IM), and one for long-distance swimmers (LD).

With respect to fatness, male 50 + 100 m FR, 1500 m FR, 50 + 100 m BR, and 200 + 400 m IM were significantly lower in SUM6SF than LD ($p < .05$). These groups were not significantly different in body mass, suggesting that LD

Table 6.1   Body Composition of Male Swimmers by Stroke and Distance

Event	n		Stature	Body mass	SUM6SF	% muscle	% skeleton	Musc: Skel
Freestyle								
50 + 100 m	47	M	186.4[a]	79.8	44.0[a]	57.8	13.3	4.3
		SD	7.5	7.1	7.1	2.6	0.9	0.4
		Min	173.6	64.3	29.3	52.6	11.0	3.6
		Max	203.5	92.0	68.8	62.8	15.0	5.2
200 + 400 m	34	M	185.2	79.1	50.4	57.0[a]	13.0	4.4
		SD	6.3	6.5	11.9	2.2	0.9	0.3
		Min	166.9	67.2	34.5	51.6	11.3	3.8
		Max	197.6	95.8	74.4	61.5	15.7	5.3
1500 m	10	M	183.1	74.3	41.8[b]	56.1[b]	13.9[a]	4.1[a-d]
		SD	8.3	9.2	9.1	3.0	0.7	0.4
		Min	166.1	61.1	31.1	51.5	12.9	3.5
		Max	197.0	92.5	61.5	59.9	15.3	4.4
Long distance	13	M	179.6	78.1	60.3[a-d]	56.3[c]	13.0	4.3
		SD	8.6	8.8	13.6	2.7	0.9	0.4
		Min	166.9	65.0	34.1	51.6	11.4	3.7
		Max	191.8	94.9	80.8	60.7	15.1	5.2
Breaststroke								
50 + 100 m	25	M	182.2	76.5	43.8[c]	59.2[a-c]	13.1	4.5[a]
		SD	6.1	6.6	10.4	2.2	0.9	0.4
		Min	172.1	65.0	31.1	54.4	10.5	4.0
		Max	193.0	88.5	81.0	63.5	14.7	5.5

	n							
200 + 400 m	12	M	180.3	76.8	48.8	59.5	13.6	4.4
		SD	6.0	6.8	18.3	3.0	0.7	0.2
		Min	166.3	61.0	30.1	54.6	12.3	3.9
		Max	187.0	85.4	99.9	64.5	14.6	4.8
Backstroke								
50 + 100 m	15	M	186.1	80.5	46.2	58.8	13.5	4.4
		SD	7.1	8.4	10.7	2.1	0.6	0.2
		Min	171.5	60.4	31.0	55.3	12.2	3.9
		Max	197.8	92.8	73.7	61.6	14.7	4.7
200 m	13	M	186.1	76.9	46.4	56.6	13.4	4.2
		SD	6.2	7.7	10.7	2.1	0.8	0.3
		Min	174.0	62.2	35.8	53.1	11.8	3.7
		Max	194.0	85.9	74.9	60.8	14.8	4.7
Butterfly								
50 + 100 m	24	M	183.3	81.2	51.0	58.5	12.9	4.5[b]
		SD	6.2	4.7	14.3	2.9	0.6	0.3
		Min	168.3	70.9	33.6	52.8	11.6	4.1
		Max	193.8	88.1	93.2	64.1	13.8	5.1
200 m	17	M	179.7[a]	76.3	47.8	57.1	12.7[a]	4.5[c]
		SD	5.3	4.9	14.5	2.9	0.7	0.3
		Min	172.4	69.6	34.2	49.8	10.7	4.0
		Max	191.9	85.1	87.6	61.0	14.0	5.4
Individual medley								
200 + 400 m	21	M	183.3	77.5	45.8[d]	57.4	12.9	4.5[d]
		SD	7.3	7.8	9.6	2.2	1.0	0.5
		Min	169.8	59.3	26.6	54.1	10.1	3.7
		Max	194.7	92.1	63.7	63.1	15.1	5.7

Note. For any measurement, common superscripts indicate which group pairs are significantly different ($p < .05$, Tukey range test). Superscripts given as a through j represent a range of superscripts: a, b, c, . . . j.

were substantially fatter than the other groups listed. For percent muscle mass, 200 + 400 m FR, 1500 m FR, and LD were significantly lower than 50 + 100 m BR. For percent skeletal mass, 1500 m FR were higher than 200 m FL. Of interest is 50 + 100 m BR, 50 + 100 m FL, 200 m FL, and 200 + 400 m IM who had a significantly higher muscle:skeletal mass ratio than 1500 m FR. The latter had low mass and low muscle:skeletal mass ratio. This reduced musculature is consistent with the need for efficient stroke production rather than power generation.

When the data were pooled by distance and examined by event only (see Table 6.2) LD were significantly fatter (higher SUM6SF) than all but FL; BR swimmers had higher percent muscle mass than LD or FR; FR and BK had higher percent skeletal mass than FL; and FL were significantly higher in muscle: skeletal mass ratio than FR.

As shown in chapter 3, there was a progressive but nonsignificant decrease in stature (186.4 cm, 185.2 cm, and 183.1 cm) and body mass (79.8 kg, 79.1 kg, and 74.3 kg) for short- to long-distance (50 + 100 m FR, 200 + 400 m FR, 1500 m FR) swimmers. LD, compared to FR, were shorter (179.6 cm) but heavier (78.1 kg) than 1500 m LD. This extra body mass appears due primarily to their greater adiposity (indicated by the SUM6SF). There were no significant differences in height or body mass between events within strokes or overall by stroke.

Differences by event distance for level and pattern of skinfold thickness in male FR are shown in Figure 6.1. LD were significantly fatter (SUM6SF = 60.3 mm) than 50 + 100 m FR (SUM6SF = 44.0 mm) and 1500 m FR (SUM6SF = 41.8 mm), but not significantly different from 200 + 400 m FR (SUM6SF = 50.0 mm). Skinfold patterning was similar at all levels of fatness, however, the 200 + 400 m FR and 1500 m FR exhibited a slightly higher front thigh skinfold thickness relative to abdominal skinfold than either the 50 + 100 m FR or LD.

Female LD had a significantly higher SUM6SF (104.6 mm) than all other groups (FR = 72.7 mm, BR = 67.2 mm, BK = 68.1 mm, FL = 71.1 mm, and IM = 71.2 mm). For percent muscle mass, all groups were significantly higher than LD; for percent skeletal mass, 50 + 100 m BR and BK, 200 + 400 m FR, and 200 m FL and BR were significantly higher than LD. There were no significant differences between any of the groups for muscle:skeletal–mass ratio. In summary, LD had substantially higher SUM6SF values and were lower in percent muscle mass and percent skeletal mass than most other event groups (see Tables 6.3 and 6.4).

Differences by event distance for level and pattern of skinfold thickness in FR are shown in Figure 6.2. LD were significantly fatter (SUM6SF = 104.6 mm) than the rest. There was little differentiation between 50 + 100 m FR (SUM6SF = 70.4 mm), 200 + 400 m FR (SUM6SF = 76.6 mm), and 800 m FR (SUM6SF = 62.3 mm). Skinfold patterning was similar at all fatness levels.

Table 6.2 Body Composition of Male Swimmers by Stroke, All Distances Combined

Event	n		Stature	Body mass	SUM6SF	% muscle	% skeleton	Musc: Skel
Freestyle	91	M	185.6[a-c]	78.9	46.1[a]	57.3[a]	13.2[a]	4.3[a]
		SD	7.2	7.3	9.9	2.5	0.9	0.4
		Min	166.1	61.1	29.3	51.5	11.0	3.5
		Max	203.5	95.8	74.4	62.8	15.7	5.3
Long distance	13	M	179.6[a]	78.1	60.3[a-d]	56.3[b]	13.0	4.3
		SD	8.6	8.8	13.6	2.7	0.9	0.4
		Min	166.9	65.0	34.1	51.6	11.4	3.7
		Max	191.8	94.9	80.8	60.7	15.1	5.2
Breaststroke	37	M	181.6[b]	76.6	45.5[b]	59.3[ab]	13.3	4.5
		SD	6.0	6.5	13.4	2.5	0.9	0.3
		Min	166.3	61.0	30.1	54.4	10.5	4.0
		Max	193.0	88.5	99.9	64.5	14.7	5.5
Backstroke	28	M	186.1	78.8	46.3[c]	57.8	13.4[b]	4.3
		SD	6.5	8.1	10.5	2.3	0.7	0.3
		Min	171.5	60.4	31.0	53.1	11.8	3.7
		Max	197.8	92.8	74.9	61.6	14.8	4.7
Butterfly	41	M	181.8[c]	79.2	49.7	57.9	12.8[ab]	4.5[a]
		SD	6.0	5.3	14.3	2.9	0.7	0.3
		Min	168.3	69.6	33.6	49.8	10.7	4.0
		Max	193.8	88.1	93.2	64.1	14.0	5.4

(continued)

Table 6.2 (*continued*)

Event	n		Stature	Body mass	SUM6SF	% muscle	% skeleton	Musc: Skel
Individual medley	21	M	183.3	77.5	45.8[d]	57.4	12.9	4.5
		SD	7.3	7.8	9.6	2.2	1.0	0.5
		Min	169.8	59.3	26.6	54.1	10.1	3.7
		Max	194.7	92.1	63.7	63.1	15.1	5.7
Total swimmers	231	M	183.8	78.4	45.8	57.8	13.1	4.4
		SD	7.1	7.1	9.5	2.6	0.9	0.4

Note. For any measurement, common superscripts indicate which group pairs are significantly different ($p < .05$, Tukey range test). Superscripts given as a through j represent a range of superscripts: a, b, c, . . .j.

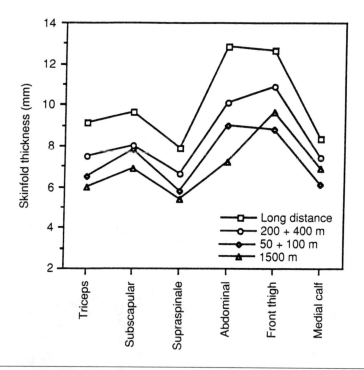

Figure 6.1   The magnitudes and patterns of six skinfolds for male freestyle swimmers by distance and primary event.

Best Versus Rest

As in the previous chapters, all swimmers ranking 1 to 12 in any of the first three events in which they participated were considered Best, the remaining swimmers, Rest. It was therefore possible to count a swimmer more than once if ranked Best in different strokes and events. Differences between the Best and Rest groups for any stroke are shown in Tables 6.5 (males) and 6.6 (females). Best male swimmers, although not significantly different from the Rest in any aspect of body composition (with the exception of percent skeletal mass for BR), were invariably somewhat taller and heavier—a pattern also true for the females.

Summary

Both males and females showed considerable variation in size among athletes in the various strokes and for events within a given stroke. When we examined athletes across all events in a stroke in his or her final placement (Best versus Rest), aside from differences in stature and body mass, there was little distinction in body composition. As observed previously, LD were the only group notably different from all other groups, including those athletes participating in the longer events within a given stroke. Both male and female LD were shorter and of

Table 6.3 Body Composition of Female Swimmers by Stroke and Distance

Event	n		Stature	Body mass	SUM6SF	% muscle	% skeleton	Musc: Skel
Freestyle								
50 + 100 m	31	M	173.9[ag]	65.0[a]	70.4[a]	51.2[a]	12.3	4.2
		SD	7.0	5.8	16.2	2.9	1.0	0.4
		Min	159.6	51.4	37.9	45.3	10.3	3.4
		Max	186.3	75.0	124.2	56.3	14.4	5.0
200 + 400 m	27	M	174.0[bh]	64.6[b]	76.6[b]	50.8[b]	12.9[a]	4.0
		SD	6.7	6.3	12.9	3.8	0.8	0.3
		Min	156.2	48.7	41.7	43.9	11.3	3.1
		Max	183.4	75.1	95.4	58.4	14.2	4.6
800 m	6	M	171.9	63.5	62.3[c]	51.6[c]	12.4	4.1
		SD	5.7	6.1	12.3	2.4	0.8	0.2
		Min	164.3	57.2	49.5	47.5	11.5	4.0
		Max	181.1	71.4	81.7	54.5	13.4	4.4
Long distance	10	M	162.6[a-f]	62.2	104.6[a-j]	46.0[a-j]	11.4[a-e]	4.0
		SD	4.6	6.7	29.8	5.0	0.8	0.4
		Min	158.0	49.8	53.5	39.3	10.3	3.4
		Max	170.2	72.5	147.1	54.5	12.8	4.5
Breaststroke								
50 + 100 m	16	M	173.6[cj]	64.0	65.3[d]	53.2[d]	12.9[b]	4.1
		SD	6.1	5.3	24.9	3.9	1.2	0.4
		Min	159.8	54.7	42.3	46.1	11.2	3.5
		Max	184.3	74.1	136.2	58.7	14.7	4.8

Event	n							
200 + 400 m	12	M	164.9^{g-j}	57.5^{ab}	69.9^{ab}	52.2^e	12.7^c	4.1
		SD	5.3	6.5	18.0	2.7	1.3	0.3
		Min	158.0	46.6	43.7	47.1	10.7	3.5
		Max	175.4	72.5	93.5	56.2	15.2	4.9
Backstroke 50 + 100 m	8	M	174.7^{di}	62.9	69.6^f	51.4^f	13.0^d	3.9
		SD	6.3	5.3	13.8	3.1	1.2	0.3
		Min	167.3	55.3	51.9	45.1	11.6	3.5
		Max	187.1	70.0	92.6	55.2	15.1	4.3
200 m	10	M	172.4^e	63.3	66.9^g	51.3^g	12.6	4.1
		SD	4.4	3.8	13.4	2.4	1.5	0.6
		Min	165.7	57.6	50.3	46.9	9.3	3.5
		Max	181.3	69.6	94.7	55.1	14.4	5.6
Butterfly 50 + 100 m	16	M	170.7	61.5	66.0^h	52.7^h	12.6	4.2
		SD	5.7	3.4	17.6	2.9	0.9	0.3
		Min	164.6	56.4	49.2	47.9	11.1	3.8
		Max	181.4	68.9	102.5	57.7	14.3	4.9
200 m	13	M	169.2	62.0	77.4^i	50.5^i	12.8^e	4.0
		SD	5.9	5.7	15.9	2.6	0.6	0.3
		Min	159.0	49.6	52.1	46.7	11.0	3.6
		Max	178.2	70.4	106.6	54.0	13.5	4.3
Individual medley 200 + 400 m	21	M	171.3^f	62.8	71.2^j	51.3^j	12.1	4.2
		SD	8.0	6.4	18.2	2.7	0.4	0.3
		Min	157.9	49.9	38.2	45.8	11.4	3.8
		Max	187.1	74.6	115.0	57.4	12.9	4.6

Note. For any measurement, common superscripts indicate which group pairs are significantly different ($p < .05$, Tukey range test). Superscripts given as a through j represent a range of superscripts: a, b, c, . . . j.

Table 6.4 Body Composition of Female Swimmers by Stroke, All Distances Combined

Event	n		Stature	Body mass	SUM6SF	% muscle	% skeleton	Musc: Skel
Freestyle	64	M	173.7[a]	64.7	72.7[a]	51.1[a]	12.6[a]	4.1
		SD	6.7	6.0	15.0	3.2	0.9	0.4
		Min	156.2	48.7	37.9	43.9	10.3	3.1
		Max	186.3	75.1	124.2	58.4	14.4	5.0
Long distance	10	M	162.6[a-e]	62.2	104.6[a-e]	46.0[a-e]	11.4[a-d]	4.0
		SD	4.6	6.7	29.8	5.0	0.8	0.4
		Min	158.0	49.8	53.5	39.3	10.3	3.4
		Max	170.2	72.5	147.1	54.5	12.8	4.5
Breaststroke	28	M	169.9[b]	61.2	67.2[b]	52.8[b]	12.9[b]	4.1
		SD	7.1	6.6	21.9	3.4	1.2	0.4
		Min	158.0	46.6	42.3	46.1	10.7	3.5
		Max	184.3	74.1	136.2	58.7	15.2	4.9

Backstroke	18	M	173.4[c]	63.1	68.1[c]	51.4[c]	12.8[c]
		SD	5.3	4.4	13.3	2.6	1.4
		Min	165.7	55.3	50.3	45.1	9.3
		Max	187.1	70.0	94.7	55.2	15.1
Butterfly	29	M	170.0[d]	61.7	71.1[d]	51.7[d]	12.7[d]
		SD	5.7	4.5	3.3	3.0	0.8
		Min	159.0	49.6	49.2	46.7	11.0
		Max	181.4	70.4	106.6	57.7	14.3
Individual medley	21	M	171.3[e]	62.8	71.2[e]	51.3[e]	12.1
		SD	8.0	6.4	18.2	2.7	0.4
		Min	157.9	49.9	38.2	45.8	11.4
		Max	187.1	74.6	115.0	57.4	12.9
Total swimmers	170	M	171.5	63.1	72.6	51.2	12.5
		SD	7.0	5.9	19.6	3.5	1.0

Note. For any measurement, common superscripts indicate which group pairs are significantly different ($p < .05$, Tukey range test). Superscripts given as a through j represent a range of superscripts: a, b, c, . . . j.

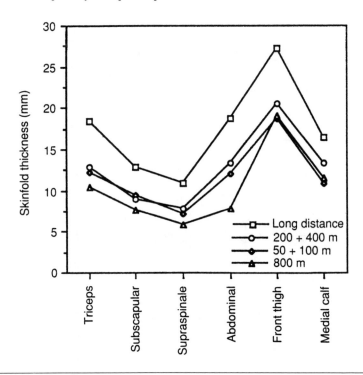

Figure 6.2   The magnitudes and patterns of six skinfolds for female freestyle swimmers by distance and primary event.

similar body mass and had a significantly higher SUM6SF than the other groups. Thus they had relatively lower percent muscle and percent skeletal masses but were no different in muscle:skeletal mass ratio.

Diving

Previous Studies

Little information is available on the body composition of Olympic divers. Carter and Yuhasz (1984) provide weight and skinfold data for 4 male divers measured at the 1976 Montreal Olympics. Their average body mass (66.7 kg) and average SUM6SF (39.8 mm) were later combined with those of 16 Olympic divers measured at the 1968 Mexico City Olympics yielding a 65.7-kg body mass and 25.0-mm SUM4 skinfolds. Body mass for 7 female Olympic divers measured at Mexico City plus 1 at Montreal was 52.8 kg, and SUM4 was 38.5 mm. No information was given regarding SUM6SF.

Results and Discussion

Similar to the analyses presented in previous chapters, divers were separated by gender and grouped according to primary event (1M, 3M, or 10M). Best divers

Table 6.5 Body Composition of Male Swimmers by Performance Rank

Event	n		Stature	Body mass	SUM6SF	% muscle	% skeleton	Musc: Skel
Freestyle 50 + 100 m								
Best	18	M	188.9[a]	81.6	45.3	57.4	13.5	4.3[a]
		SD	7.9	6.6	8.1	2.8	0.8	0.4
Rest	40	M	184.3[a]	78.8	45.1	58.3	13.2	4.4[a]
		SD	6.6	7.1	8.6	2.6	0.9	0.4
200 + 400 m								
Best	17	M	188.7[b]	82.3[a]	49.9	57.4	13.0	4.4
		SD	5.3	5.7	10.8	2.4	0.7	0.2
Rest	39	M	183.6[b]	76.7[a]	48.4	56.6	13.5	4.2
		SD	8.0	7.6	12.1	2.2	1.1	0.4
1500 m								
Best	7	M	187.3	78.6	44.3	56.5	13.6	4.2
		SD	5.9	7.3	8.4	2.6	1.0	0.3
Rest	10	M	181.7	74.4	55.0	55.3	13.2	4.2
		SD	8.7	9.0	18.1	2.3	1.0	0.5
Long distance								
Best	4	M	181.3	79.9	60.3	56.6	12.7	4.5
		SD	7.7	5.9	11.0	2.6	1.1	0.6
Rest	9	M	178.8	77.2	60.3	56.2	13.2	4.3
		SD	9.3	10.1	15.2	2.9	0.9	0.3
Breaststroke								
Best	21	M	183.5[c]	79.2[b]	43.4	60.2	13.3[a]	4.5
		SD	5.4	6.5	8.0	2.5	0.7	0.3

(continued)

Table 6.5 (*continued*)

Event	n		Stature	Body mass	SUM6SF	% muscle	% skeleton	Musc: Skel
Rest	18	M	178.5[c]	72.8[b]	48.7	58.2	12.9[a]	4.5
		SD	5.9	5.2	17.6	2.0	1.3	0.5
Backstroke 50 + 100 m								
Best	17	M	188.1[d]	80.9	44.6	57.6	13.3	4.3
		SD	6.3	7.7	7.7	2.3	0.6	0.2
Rest	20	M	182.8[d]	76.4	48.5	57.7	13.2	4.4
		SD	6.5	7.2	14.7	3.1	1.0	0.5
Butterfly 50 + 100 m								
Best	22	M	184.5[e]	80.2	45.7	58.4	13.0	4.5
		SD	6.0	6.0	10.0	2.7	0.7	0.3
Rest	29	M	180.0[e]	77.2	51.8	58.0	12.9	4.5
		SD	6.4	5.5	15.5	3.0	0.7	0.3
Individual medley								
Best	12	M	187.1	80.2	43.6	57.5	13.2	4.4
		SD	6.8	8.4	10.0	2.6	0.4	0.2
Rest	23	M	182.8	76.9	44.9	58.2	12.9	4.6
		SD	7.5	8.2	7.6	2.4	1.2	0.5

Note. For any measurement, common superscripts indicate values which are significantly different ($p < .05$) for Best versus Rest groups within any given stroke and distance.

Table 6.6 Body Composition of Female Swimmers by Performance Rank

Event	n		Stature	Body mass	SUM6SF	% muscle	% skeleton	Musc: Skel
Freestyle								
50 + 100 m								
Best	17	M	175.1	64.7	65.6	51.8	12.9[a]	4.0
		SD	6.1	5.4	12.7	3.4	0.7	0.4
Rest	29	M	171.2	63.4	74.5	50.8	12.2[a]	4.2
		SD	6.3	5.6	17.4	3.4	1.0	0.4
200 + 400 m								
Best	20	M	176.1[a]	66.3	72.2	50.7	12.6	4.0
		SD	4.7	4.6	13.8	3.4	1.1	0.3
Rest	23	M	171.4[a]	63.1	73.0	51.8	12.8	4.1
		SD	6.8	6.3	13.6	3.3	0.8	0.4
800 m								
Best	9	M	175.1	66.3	70.8	51.1	12.4	4.2
		SD	4.2	6.1	13.6	2.8	0.7	0.3
Rest	6	M	171.7	63.3	77.8	49.9	12.8	4.0
		SD	8.0	4.8	15.2	2.0	0.8	0.3
Long distance								
Best	4	M	166.8[b]	60.5	87.4	47.2	11.7	4.1
		SD	4.3	8.5	29.6	4.3	0.9	0.4
Rest	6	M	159.8[b]	63.4	116.0	45.1	11.1	4.0
		SD	2.1	5.8	26.1	5.6	0.7	0.4

(continued)

Table 6.6 (continued)

Event	n		Stature	Body mass	SUM6SF	% muscle	% skeleton	Musc: Skel
Breaststroke								
50 + 100 m								
Best	19	M	171.0	62.3	64.6	53.1	13.0	4.1
		SD	8.0	7.5	23.6	3.8	1.2	0.4
Rest	9	M	167.5	60.0	72.8	52.1	12.6	4.2
		SD	4.3	3.3	6.0	2.6	1.3	0.3
Backstroke								
50 + 100 m								
Best	14	M	171.9	64.3	66.6	51.5	12.8	4.1
		SD	5.2	4.3	12.4	2.8	1.4	0.6
Rest	11	M	174.3	62.9	74.6	50.8	12.6	4.0
		SD	6.0	3.6	21.4	3.2	0.8	0.4
Butterfly								
50 + 100 m								
Best	21	M	171.9[c]	62.9	64.4[a]	53.0[a]	12.8	4.2
		SD	5.4	3.8	16.8	2.8	0.8	0.3
Rest	19	M	168.3[c]	60.9	77.4[a]	50.1[a]	12.4	4.1
		SD	4.8	4.1	15.4	2.3	0.7	0.3
Individual medley								
Best	16	M	174.5	64.9	65.3	52.2	12.3	4.2
		SD	8.8	6.7	12.7	2.9	0.7	0.3
Rest	15	M	169.4	61.3	72.5	51.2	12.4	4.2
		SD	6.7	4.8	5.6	3.0	0.8	0.3

Note. For any measurement, common superscripts indicate values which are sigificantly different ($p < .05$) for Best versus Rest groups within any given stroke and distance.

were those who placed from 1 to 10 in any of the three events; those who placed 11th or lower were designated Rest. Stature, body mass, and body composition values by primary event and performance are given in Tables 6.7 (females) and 6.8 (males).

Although the female divers were not significantly different from one another by event, 1M and 3M divers had larger SUM6SF (1M = 71.9 mm, 3M = 66.5 mm) than 10M divers (SUM6SF = 60.3). For the Best versus Rest only percent skeletal mass was significantly higher in the Best group.

Data reported by Carter and Yuhasz (1984) for 8 divers from previous Olympics were found similar to 39 female divers measured in this study (body mass = 53.7 kg) in triceps skinfold (11.4 mm vs. 10.9 mm), subscapular skinfold (8.5 mm vs. 9.1 mm), supraspinale skinfold (6.8 mm vs. 8.1 mm), and medial calf skinfold (9.7 mm vs. 10.5 mm) (see Table 6.16). The SUM4 values were similar for both female groups (present = 37.5 mm vs. previous = 38.6 mm).

For the males, there were no significant differences in body composition values between events or for the Best versus Rest groups. Compared to previous data reported by Carter and Yuhasz (1984), the 43 male divers (body mass = 66.7 kg) measured in the present study were higher in SUM6SF than 4 divers measured in Montreal (45.9 mm vs. 39.8 mm). Compared to 20 divers from the Mexico City and Montreal Olympics, the present divers were similar in triceps skinfold (6.8 mm vs. 6.2 mm), subscapular skinfold (7.9 mm vs. 8.0 mm), supraspinale skinfold (6.0 mm vs. 5.8 mm), and medial calf skinfold (6.0 mm vs. 5.1 mm) (see Table 6.15). The SUM4 was 29.2 mm in the Perth divers and 25.1 mm in the previous male Olympic divers.

Summary

Few distinctions in body composition values were seen between events or by Best versus Rest groups for either female or male divers.

Synchronized Swimming

Previous Studies

Like several other aquatic sports, there are few data available on synchronized swimmers. Moffat, Katch, Freedson, and Lindeman (1980) reported stature, body mass, and percent fat for 15 members of the University of Michigan synchronized swimming team, which placed second in the 1978 National Association of Intercollegiate Athletics for Women Championships. Average stature, body mass, and percent fat (by hydrodensitometry) for these women were 165.5 cm, 57.2 kg, and 20.9% fat, respectively. Poole, Crepin, and Sevigny (1980) reported the stature and body mass of two Canadian national swimming teams: 165.6 cm and 54.9 kg (Calgary) and 163.8 cm and 55.3 kg (Quebec). No fat level was indicated. Hawes and Sovak (1993) reported a stature of 165.2 cm, body mass of 58.7 kg, and percent fat of 20.5% for 14 Canadian national team SS.

Table 6.7 Body Composition of Female Divers by Primary Event and Performance Rank

Event	n		Stature	Body mass	SUM6SF	% muscle	% skeleton	Musc: Skel
1M	13	M	160.2	54.7	71.9	52.1	12.3	4.3
		SD	5.4	4.7	18.9	3.8	1.3	0.6
		Min	153.5	46.7	51.9	46.1	9.5	3.6
		Max	170.3	61.9	114.3	57.7	13.7	5.6
3M	9	M	160.8	54.6	66.5	51.0	11.6	4.5
		SD	5.4	3.8	5.6	3.0	1.6	0.7
		Min	152.0	49.5	61.3	46.4	9.7	3.6
		Max	167.8	59.7	79.6	56.4	14.0	5.8
10M	17	M	162.1	52.5	60.3	52.3	12.4	4.3
		SD	6.9	6.6	18.5	4.2	1.6	0.6
		Min	145.1	37.3	32.1	43.8	9.8	3.2
		Max	173.0	65.6	93.5	62.0	14.7	5.2
Total	39	M	161.2	53.7	65.6	51.9	12.2	4.3
		SD	6.0	5.5	17.0	3.8	1.5	0.6
		Min	145.1	37.3	32.1	43.8	9.5	3.2
		Max	173.0	65.6	114.3	62.0	14.7	5.8
Best	19	M	160.7	52.2	62.0	52.8	12.9[a]	4.2
		SD	5.8	5.3	16.5	3.9	1.2	0.6
Rest	20	M	161.7	55.2	69.0	51.1	11.6[a]	4.4
		SD	6.3	5.3	17.2	3.6	1.5	0.6

Note. For any measurement, common superscripts indicate which group pairs are significantly different ($p < .05$, Tukey range test).

Table 6.8   Body Composition of Male Divers by Primary Event and Performance Rank

Event	n		Stature	Body mass	SUM6SF	% muscle	% skeleton	Musc: Skel
1M	19	M	168.7	65.2	44.1	59.1	13.0	4.6
		SD	7.5	10.1	10.4	2.6	1.6	0.6
		Min	149.1	41.5	28.0	55.4	9.6	3.5
		Max	182.2	81.5	65.6	64.9	16.0	6.0
3M	10	M	173.1	69.5	47.8	59.8	12.5	4.9
		SD	7.2	6.8	14.5	3.4	1.5	0.7
		Min	161.1	58.4	31.3	55.2	9.6	3.9
		Max	184.0	78.5	79.7	65.6	14.8	6.2
10M	14	M	172.5	66.8	47.0	57.1	13.0	4.4
		SD	10.6	12.5	10.7	4.5	1.2	0.5
		Min	145.2	37.6	33.4	47.5	10.9	3.2
		Max	189.9	86.3	64.0	65.5	14.6	5.1
Total	43	M	170.9	66.7	45.9	58.6	12.9	4.6
		SD	8.6	10.2	11.4	3.6	1.4	0.6
		Min	145.2	37.6	28.0	47.5	9.6	3.2
		Max	189.9	86.3	79.7	65.6	16.0	6.2
Best	19	M	170.2	65.4	44.6	58.5	13.0	4.5
		SD	8.7	9.6	12.9	3.9	1.0	0.6
Rest	24	M	171.5	67.7	46.8	58.7	12.8	4.7
		SD	8.7	10.8	10.1	3.4	1.6	0.6

Note. There were no significant differences between groups for any measurement.

Results and Discussion

As in previous chapters, SS were grouped according to primary event—solo, duet, or team—and by team place in competition. Stature, body mass, and body composition values by primary event and performance are given in Table 6.9 and by team in Table 6.10. There were no significant differences between events for any body composition measurement.

Compared with the previous studies cited, SS measured in this study (body mass = 56.7 kg) were somewhat lighter than the swimmers reported by Moffat et al. (1980) (57.2 kg), somewhat heavier than the Calgary and Quebec swimmers reported by Poole et al. (1980) (54.9 kg and 55.3 kg, respectively), and lighter than swimmers reported by Hawes and Sovak (1993) (58.7 kg). The 20.5% estimated fat value in the latter study (method or equation used not reported) was somewhat higher than the 16.2% value derived in this study from the average SUM6SF (81.7 mm) using the modified formula of Yuhasz (Carter, 1982b). Hawes and Sovak also estimated a skeletal mass of 14.5% compared to our 12.3% value and a muscle mass of 37.9% compared to our 49.6% value. They used the methods of Matiegka (1921) for estimating skeletal and muscle masses. The value for percent fat reported by Hawes and Sovak is similar to that reported earlier by Moffat et al. (20.9%). Both values are higher than the 16.2% reported here which may be somewhat low. Given that swimmers in this study were both taller and lighter than the swimmers reported by Moffat et al. and Hawes and Sovak, this value is not unreasonable.

Best Versus Rest

Swimmers who ranked 1 through 10 in the solo and duet events were considered Best and the remainder, Rest. The three top ranked in the team event were considered Best, the remaining teams, Rest. There were no significant differences in any measurement between Best versus Rest solo and duet events, or between the medalists and the remaining teams.

For the various teams by final place, the Netherlands, Australian, and Chinese teams were significantly higher in SUM6SF than the Spanish team; the Netherlands team was also significantly higher than the Japanese team. For percent muscle mass, the British, Netherlands, and Chinese teams were lower than the Spanish team; and the British and Netherlands teams were also lower than the Japanese team. For percent skeletal mass, all other teams were higher than the New Zealand team; for muscle:skeletal mass ratio, all other teams except the Japanese team were significantly lower than the New Zealand team; the Netherlands, Swiss, British, Australian, and Italian teams were also lower than the Japanese team. The Canadian, American, and Spanish teams had a higher muscle:skeletal mass ratio than the Netherlands team.

Summary

As reported for swimming, there was substantial variation for SS in the various events and among teams. There was no apparent trend in body composition measurements related to success in synchronized swimming. The hypothesis that a somewhat greater body fatness in the Best group might provide an added performance advantage (from increased buoyancy) was not supported by this

Table 6.9   Body Composition of Synchronized Swimmers by Event and Performance Rank

Event	n		Stature	Body mass	SUM6SF	% muscle	% skeleton	Musc: Skel
Solo	19	M	169.0[a]	57.5	76.1	49.6	12.6	4.0
		SD	3.9	4.3	18.7	3.4	0.9	0.4
		Min	158.8	51.3	50.5	43.2	11.0	3.2
		Max	176.6	65.3	112.6	54.7	14.0	4.7
Duet	24	M	166.4	57.2	86.4	48.7	12.4	3.9
		SD	4.6	4.7	20.9	3.2	0.8	0.3
		Min	159.4	47.1	37.5	42.0	10.2	3.2
		Max	173.9	65.4	128.9	53.6	14.1	4.4
Team	94	M	165.2[a]	56.4	81.6	48.7	12.5	3.9
		SD	6.3	5.6	22.9	3.9	1.2	0.5
		Min	151.9	43.9	40.2	36.9	8.7	3.0
		Max	180.5	72.3	145.8	58.7	16.6	5.2
Total	137	M	166.0	56.7	81.7	48.8	12.5	3.9
		SD	5.8	5.3	22.1	3.7	1.1	0.4
		Min	151.9	43.9	37.5	36.9	8.7	3.0
		Max	180.5	72.3	145.8	58.7	16.6	5.2
Solo and duet								
Best	25	M	167.2	57.6	81.4	49.0	12.6	3.9
		SD	4.8	4.6	21.3	3.6	0.8	0.4
Rest	18	M	168.1	56.9	82.5	49.6	12.5	4.0
		SD	3.9	5.0	19.6	2.8	0.9	0.3

Note. For any measurement, common superscripts indicate which group pairs are significantly different ($p < .05$, Tukey range test).

Table 6.10   Body Composition of Synchronized Swimmers According to Place in the Team Event

Team	Place	n		Stature	Body mass	SUM6SF	% muscle	% skeleton	Musc: Skel
USA	1	10	M	164.3	56.4	82.3	49.8	12.3[a]	4.1[ar]
			SD	5.4	2.7	12.9	3.0	0.4	0.3
Canada	2	9	M	170.6	61.4	84.7	48.4	12.2[b]	4.0[bq]
			SD	4.1	2.9	20.2	3.1	0.5	0.3
Japan	3	8	M	160.7	52.1	63.7[d]	52.4[de]	12.3[c]	4.3[l-p]
			SD	4.8	4.2	12.5	3.4	0.7	0.5
USSR	4	9	M	168.4	56.8	69.1	49.9	13.1[d]	3.8[c]
			SD	5.7	5.5	18.4	3.2	1.2	0.4
France	5	9	M	167.2	56.6	82.1	48.1	12.7[e]	3.8[d]
			SD	4.2	4.3	17.9	2.2	0.5	0.1
China	6	7	M	162.0	54.9	94.3[c]	46.8[c]	12.0[f]	3.9[e]
			SD	2.9	3.7	13.1	1.5	0.5	0.2
Italy	7	10	M	163.2	56.4	79.9	48.0	12.7[g]	3.8[fl]
			SD	8.0	6.4	18.9	2.9	0.7	0.1

Britain	8	9	M	164.1	57.6	87.1	44.8[ad]	12.2[h]	3.7[gm]
			SD	6.2	6.1	14.6	3.8	1.4	0.2
Netherlands	9	10	M	168.2	55.7	99.2[ad]	46.1[be]	13.3[i]	3.5[hn]
			SD	3.8	5.2	33.8	3.3	1.5	0.2[q-s]
Switzerland	10	10	M	170.7	58.9	86.2	47.5	13.2[j]	3.6[io]
			SD	6.1	6.4	25.2	3.8	0.7	0.4
Australia	11	9	M	165.9	55.4	95.3[b]	48.1	13.0[k]	3.7[jp]
			SD	4.3	4.4	21.7	5.1	0.8	0.4
Spain	12	8	M	164.7	55.5	55.6[a-c]	52.7[a-c]	13.0[l]	4.1[ks]
			SD	3.1	5.0	21.3	2.5	0.9	0.4
New Zealand	13	10	M	164.2	55.4	79.7	48.2	10.4[a-l]	4.6[a-k]
			SD	6.9	7.0	21.3	3.4	0.8	0.3
Total	1-13	118	M	165.8	56.5	81.8	48.4	12.5	3.9
			SD	5.9	5.3	22.7	3.8	1.1	0.4

Note. For any measurement, common superscripts indicate which team pairs are significantly different ($p < .05$, Tukey range test). Superscripts given as a through j represent a range of superscripts: a, b, c, . . . j.

study. It may be that success in this sport is exclusively dependent on skill, more so than in the swimming events, where body size and composition appear to influence success.

Water Polo

Previous Studies

Although there are several studies on male water polo players, few of them have assessed body composition. Carter and Yuhasz (1984) summarized skinfold data measured on 71 players in the 1986 Mexico City Olympics, and 10 players in the 1972 Munich Olympics. In Mexico City values for the athletes' triceps, subscapular, supraspinale, and medial calf skinfolds were 8.1 mm, 11.7 mm, 9.6 mm, 7.1 mm, respectively. For athletes measured in Munich, values for the triceps, subscapular, iliac crest, and medial calf skinfolds were 8.0 mm, 9.8 mm, 13.4 mm, and 7.3 mm, respectively. Values for the triceps, subscapular, supraspinale, iliac crest, and medial calf skinfolds for the present study were 9.2 mm, 9.9 mm, 8.2 mm, 13.4 mm, and 7.9 mm, respectively (see Table 6.15). The SUM6SF for athletes at Munich was 61.0 mm; SUM6SF for athletes at Montreal was not given. There are no previous data on international-level female water polo players.

Results and Discussion

WP were analyzed by team place in competition and playing position for each gender. Players classified themselves as primarily GK, CB, CF, and offensive or defensive wings (combined as "other" field players), or OTH. Body composition values for each position are given in Tables 6.11 (males) and 6.12 (females) and by team in Tables 6.13 (males) and 6.14 (females).

Comparisons by Position

There were no significant differences in SUM6SF values, percent muscle mass, or muscle:skeletal mass ratio between any of the positions for males. However, GK were significantly higher in percent skeletal mass than CF. For all players combined, the SUM6SF was 62.5 mm, a value similar to that (61.0 mm) reported for male WP measured in Munich, 1972.

For female WP there were no significant differences between groups for any body composition measurements. For all players combined, the SUM6SF was 89.8 mm.

Comparisons by Team

For the males there were no significant differences in percent muscle mass between the teams. For percent skeletal mass the French team was significantly higher than the Chinese and Egyptian teams; for muscle:skeletal mass ratio the Chinese team was significantly higher than the French team.

The German female team had sigificantly higher SUM6SF than the French team. There were no significant differences for any other body composition measurements among the teams.

Table 6.11 Body Composition of Male Water Polo Players According to Position

Playing position	n		Stature	Body mass	SUM6SF	% muscle	% skeleton	Musc: Skel
Goalkeepers	30	M	189.1[b]	86.2	60.9	56.6	13.1[a]	4.3
		SD	5.9	8.1	19.0	3.2	0.9	0.4
		Min	173.0	75.1	27.9	48.4	10.7	3.7
		Max	200.8	105.6	107.2	62.3	15.3	5.2
Center backs	25	M	189.2[c]	90.2[a]	65.0	56.9	12.7	4.5
		SD	6.1	8.0	18.3	3.2	0.7	0.3
		Min	176.1	77.7	35.4	49.6	11.7	3.9
		Max	205.9	105.5	96.0	62.7	14.4	5.1
Center forwards	40	M	188.8[a]	91.4[b]	68.3	55.5	12.6[a]	4.4
		SD	6.3	8.7	19.2	3.2	1.0	0.4
		Min	177.0	69.9	32.0	49.2	10.6	3.6
		Max	201.4	112.5	112.1	61.5	14.7	5.4
Others	95	M	184.0[a-c]	82.7[ab]	59.9	55.8	12.8	4.4
		SD	5.9	6.9	16.0	3.2	0.8	0.3
		Min	171.4	66.1	32.2	47.7	11.0	3.7
		Max	197.3	99.7	100.9	65.3	14.4	5.2
Total	190	M	186.5	86.1	62.5	56.0	12.8	4.4
		SD	6.5	8.5	17.7	3.2	0.8	0.3
		Min	171.4	66.1	27.9	47.7	10.6	3.6
		Max	205.9	112.5	112.1	65.3	15.3	5.4

Note. For any measurement, common superscripts indicate which group pairs are sigificantly different ($p < .05$, Tukey range test). Superscripts given as a through j represent a range of superscripts: a, b, c, . . . j.

Table 6.12 Body Composition of Female Water Polo Players According to Position

Playing position	n		Stature	Body mass	SUM6SF	% muscle	% skeleton	Musc: Skel
Goalkeepers	14	M	175.1	66.0	94.3	50.2	12.7	4.0
		SD	6.4	7.6	22.6	1.9	0.7	0.3
		Min	165.5	50.3	61.4	47.8	11.6	3.5
		Max	189.2	76.3	151.6	54.0	14.2	4.5
Center backs	9	M	172.4	67.5	98.5	48.6	12.2	4.0
		SD	2.6	6.1	23.7	2.7	0.8	0.2
		Min	168.1	57.9	58.7	44.5	11.3	3.8
		Max	176.5	76.8	138.0	52.7	14.0	4.5
Center forwards	27	M	173.3	69.0[a]	96.8	49.2	12.2	4.1
		SD	5.3	7.5	25.2	3.2	0.9	0.3
		Min	163.8	55.5	55.6	44.1	10.5	3.4
		Max	183.2	82.0	133.5	58.9	13.7	4.8
Others*	46	M	170.3	62.5[a]	87.5	49.0	12.6	3.9
		SD	5.8	5.8	20.8	3.0	0.8	0.3
		Min	157.0	51.6	95.5	41.8	10.5	3.3
		Max	185.4	77.1	149.8	56.8	13.9	4.6
Total**	109	M	171.3	64.8	89.8	49.3	12.3	4.0
		SD	5.9	7.2	23.8	2.9	0.8	0.3
		Min	157.0	49.7	39.7	41.8	10.3	3.4
		Max	189.2	82.0	151.6	58.9	14.0	4.8

Note. For any measurement, common superscripts indicate which group pairs are significantly different ($p < .05$, Tukey range test). *13 players not included, no position given; **all players included.

Best Versus Rest

Of the 16 male teams participating, only the first-place team members were not measured; therefore, the second- through fourth-ranked teams (Spain, Hungary, and the USA) were considered Best; the seven lowest ranked teams (Greece, Cuba, France, Canada, China, Egypt, and New Zealand) were considered Rest. There were no significant differences in any body composition measurements between these two groups.

For the females, the top four finishers (the Netherlands, Canada, USA, and Hungary) were considered the Best and the remaining teams (Australia, Germany, New Zealand, Brazil, and France), the Rest. There were no significant differences between Best and Rest groups for any of the body composition measurements.

Summary

Similar to the aquatic sports discussed previously, for both male and female WP there was little differentiation between position or by team event.

Concluding Remarks

Figures 6.3 (males) and 6.4 (females) show the skinfold patterning and relative level of adiposity for athletes in all four sports.

Male WP were similar in skinfold patterning and thicknesses to male LD with the exception of the abdominal skinfold. The SUM6SF for WP was 62.5 mm compared to 60.3 mm for LD. Female WP were also similar in skinfold patterning to LD; however, unlike the males, they had a lower SUM6SF value (89.8 mm) than LD (104.6 mm).

For male and female divers and swimmers, skinfold patterning and level of adiposity were virtually identical. For the male divers SUM6SF was 45.9 mm; for the swimmers SUM6SF was 45.8 mm. For the female divers SUM6SF was 65.6 mm; for the swimmers SUM6SF was 72.6 mm.

SS had a higher SUM6SF (81.7 mm) than other swimmers but not as high as WP or LD.

Skinfold thicknesses by sport are shown in Tables 6.15 (males) and 6.16 (females). These values correspond to the data shown in Figures 6.3 and 6.4 with the addition of biceps and iliac crest skinfolds. No group comparisons were made.

It is difficult to assess whether the greater adiposity (as indicated by the higher SUM6SF) shown by SS relative to the other swimmers reflects a physical advantage or simply the aesthetics of the sport. But it is possible that the adiposity of WP compared to the other swimmers may represent a physical advantage in terms of buoyancy. For LD it is likely that adiposity provides both the physical and physiological advantages of buoyancy, energy stores, and insulation.

In general, across all the aquatic sports examined, a wide variation in physique is apparent, and success within any sport at this level of competition is less likely to be dependent on body size and composition than on experience and skill.

Table 6.13   Body Composition of Male Water Polo Players According to Team and Place

Team	Place	n		Stature	Body mass	SUM6SF	% muscle	% skeleton	Musc: Skel
Spain	2	13	M	182.8	79.1	61.4	55.4	13.0	4.3
			SD	6.0	6.4	12.4	2.6	0.6	0.3
Hungary	3	13	M	188.8	90.6	59.6	56.6	12.7	4.5
			SD	5.6	9.6	15.3	3.0	0.6	0.3
USA	4	11	M	192.0	89.1	62.2	56.1	12.9	4.4
			SD	7.2	9.8	14.9	2.0	0.6	0.3
Germany	5	13	M	191.3	90.6	65.9	55.7	12.9	4.3
			SD	4.5	8.0	16.5	2.5	0.8	0.3
Italy	6	12	M	184.6	82.6	51.3	55.9	13.0	4.3
			SD	5.7	7.3	12.1	2.8	1.0	0.4
USSR	7	13	M	188.9	88.6	54.7	57.3	12.9	4.5
			SD	5.3	5.7	20.1	4.7	0.7	0.4
Australia	8	13	M	189.6	91.7	76.2	53.9	12.6	4.3
			SD	5.6	6.5	16.3	2.9	0.8	0.2
Romania	9	12	M	186.5	85.4	62.8	54.8	12.7	4.3
			SD	4.6	5.5	10.2	2.3	0.8	0.3

Greece	10	M	184.4	88.2	68.7	56.0	12.9	4.4
		SD	7.3	10.0	22.8	3.7	0.8	0.4
Cuba	11	M	186.9	88.8	66.7	57.5	12.6	4.6
		SD	5.7	7.6	17.0	2.9	1.0	0.4
France	12	M	187.3	82.3	63.6	56.4	13.5[ab]	4.2[a]
		SD	8.4	7.9	15.2	3.3	0.6	0.3
Canada	13	M	187.1	86.3	64.7	56.2	12.9	4.4
		SD	4.0	6.0	14.3	2.3	0.6	0.3
China	14	M	183.6	83.5	65.4	57.3	12.3[a]	4.7[a]
		SD	3.6	6.6	24.8	3.9	0.8	0.3
Egypt	15	M	181.7	81.9	58.4	54.7	12.4[b]	4.4
		SD	4.8	9.5	16.5	3.8	1.1	0.4
New Zealand	16	M	182.9	82.6	55.2	56.6	12.9	4.4
		SD	7.9	9.1	23.3	3.3	1.1	0.4
Best	37	M	187.6	86.1	61.0	56.0	12.9	4.4
		SD	7.2	10.0	13.9	2.5	0.6	0.3
Rest	78	M	185.0	85.0	62.9	56.2	12.9	4.4
		SD	6.7	8.7	18.5	3.3	0.9	0.4

Note. For any measurement, common superscripts indicate which team pairs are significantly different ($p < .05$, Tukey range test).

Table 6.14 Body Composition of Female Water Polo Players According to Team and Place

Team	Place	n		Stature	Body mass	SUM6SF	% muscle	% skeleton	Musc: Skel
Netherlands	1	13	M	176.4[bc]	70.1	98.3	48.8	12.5	3.9
			SD	6.3	8.8	34.2	2.3	0.7	0.3
Canada	2	11	M	168.9	64.0	81.8	49.0	12.2	4.0
			SD	6.6	6.7	21.5	2.8	0.9	0.3
USA	3	12	M	169.1	60.8	77.4	51.0	13.1	3.9
			SD	6.0	7.3	21.0	4.1	0.8	0.3
Hungary	4	12	M	173.1	64.9	93.8	49.6	12.2	4.1
			SD	3.1	4.1	22.7	2.9	0.7	0.3
Australia	5	13	M	172.9	65.1	87.7	49.1	12.5	3.9
			SD	3.8	6.2	15.9	3.5	0.6	0.3
Germany	6	8	M	175.9[a]	70.5	105.8[a]	48.9	12.5	3.9
			SD	4.3	6.5	17.0	1.6	0.8	0.3
New Zealand	7	14	M	173.1	67.5	96.6	48.2	12.3	3.9
			SD	5.4	6.6	16.9	2.5	0.9	0.3
Brazil	8	13	M	167.4[c]	60.9	97.9	49.2	12.4	4.0
			SD	3.4	4.4	19.1	2.5	1.0	0.4
France	9	13	M	166.3[ab]	61.4	73.0[a]	50.1	12.6	4.0
			SD	4.4	7.5	25.9	2.9	1.0	0.3
Best		48	M	172.0	65.1	88.2	49.6	12.5	4.0
			SD	6.4	7.6	26.4	3.1	0.8	0.3
Rest		61	M	170.8	64.7	91.2	49.1	12.5	4.0
			SD	5.4	7.0	21.7	2.7	0.9	0.3

Note. For any measurement, common superscripts indicate which team pairs are significantly different ($p < .05$, Tukey range test).

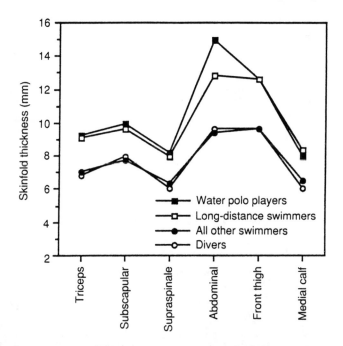

Figure 6.3   The magnitudes and patterns of six skinfolds for male athletes in diving, swimming, and water polo.

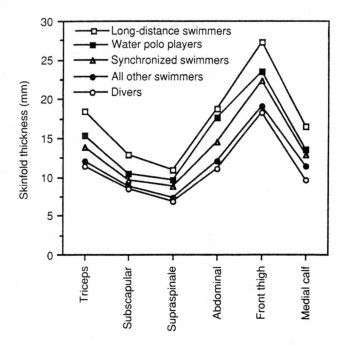

Figure 6.4   The magnitudes and patterns of six skinfolds for female athletes in diving, swimming, synchronized swimming, and water polo.

Table 6.15 Skinfold Thickness for Males by Sport

Sport	n		TCPS	SSCAP	SSPNL	ABDM	FTHI	MCALF	BCPS	ILCR
Swimming	218	M	7.0	7.9	6.3	9.4	9.6	6.5	3.7	9.2
		SD	2.0	1.7	2.0	4.2	2.8	2.0	0.8	3.3
		Min	3.9	5.3	3.5	3.9	4.9	3.0	2.5	4.9
		Max	16.3	20.6	19.2	33.4	18.7	13.6	9.9	23.2
Long-distance swimming	13	M	9.0	9.6	7.9	12.8	12.6	8.3	4.1	11.3
		SD	2.3	2.5	2.7	4.9	3.8	2.3	1.0	3.9
		Min	6.2	6.2	3.6	4.8	7.2	4.7	2.5	5.6
		Max	12.6	14.6	14.0	21.2	21.7	11.9	5.7	18.6
Diving	43	M	6.8	7.9	6.0	9.6	9.6	6.0	3.8	8.5
		SD	2.1	1.8	1.6	3.5	3.1	1.8	0.8	2.2
		Min	4.1	5.2	3.8	5.1	4.9	3.2	2.6	5.0
		Max	12.3	12.0	10.9	17.7	18.9	11.6	6.1	13.0
Water polo	190	M	9.2	9.9	8.2	14.9	12.6	7.9	4.3	13.4
		SD	3.1	2.6	3.1	6.3	4.5	2.9	1.2	5.3
		Min	3.8	6.1	4.3	5.0	4.4	2.7	2.6	4.5
		Max	18.9	23.1	20.2	35.8	31.7	19.2	10.2	30.1

Note. Skinfolds (mm) are triceps (TCPS), subscapular (SSCAP), supraspinale (SSPNL), abdominal (ABDM), front thigh (FTHI), medial calf (MCALF), biceps (BCPS), and iliac crest (ILCR). No group comparisons were made.

Table 6.16 Skinfold Thickness for Females by Sport

Sport	n		TCPS	SSCAP	SSPNL	ABDM	FTHI	MCALF	BCPS	ILCR
Swimming	160	M	12.1	8.8	7.3	12.1	19.1	11.4	5.9	9.8
		SD	3.3	2.9	2.3	5.0	5.6	3.4	1.9	3.7
		Min	6.4	5.1	3.7	4.6	8.9	3.6	2.4	4.4
		Max	21.7	26.4	20.0	30.0	37.6	20.9	14.8	25.7
Long-distance swimming	10	M	18.4	12.9	10.9	18.8	27.3	16.5	8.4	15.2
		SD	4.3	6.0	4.4	8.8	8.6	3.6	3.1	6.4
		Min	9.4	7.0	4.6	6.3	15.6	10.6	4.2	5.7
		Max	22.3	25.1	16.8	31.4	44.4	21.8	13.3	26.3
Diving	39	M	11.4	8.5	6.8	11.1	18.2	9.7	4.9	7.9
		SD	3.2	2.2	2.0	3.8	6.4	4.0	1.2	2.8
		Min	5.6	3.8	2.9	3.8	8.6	4.3	2.7	3.3
		Max	20.4	14.0	10.7	20.0	34.0	21.0	7.4	16.6
Synchronized swimming	137	M	13.8	9.6	8.8	14.5	22.3	12.9	6.1	10.8
		SD	3.7	2.9	3.6	6.2	6.4	4.4	2.1	4.3
		Min	6.0	5.1	3.5	4.3	10.5	5.8	2.8	4.1
		Max	25.1	17.7	19.2	31.4	41.8	25.0	13.8	23.8
Water polo	109	M	15.3	10.5	9.6	17.6	23.4	13.5	7.1	12.1
		SD	4.3	3.6	3.4	7.4	6.2	4.0	2.7	4.9
		Min	7.2	5.2	3.5	4.3	11.5	5.9	2.8	3.7
		Max	29.4	24.4	17.8	40.0	38.2	23.0	16.4	24.2

Note. Skinfolds (mm) are triceps (TCPS), subscapular (SSCAP), supraspinale (SSPNL), abdominal (ABDM), front thigh (FTHI), medial calf (MCALF), biceps (BCPS), and iliac crest (ILCR). No group comparisons were made.

Chapter 7

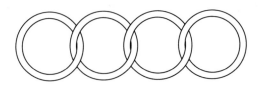

Summary and Implications

Timothy R. Ackland, Juan C. Mazza, and J.E. Lindsay Carter

Before the successful execution of the Kinanthropometric Aquatic Sports Project in Perth in December 1990 and January 1991, few objective data were available to describe the morphology of current champions in swimming, diving, synchronized swimming, and water polo. By publishing these initial results we anticipated meeting the following objectives:

- To provide descriptive data of the physical characteristics of participants at the World Championships
- To provide a breakdown by sport, gender, and event or playing position
- To compare performers who excelled with others of lower ranking to identify aspects of morphology that may be optimal for each event or position within a sport
- To seek evidence for morphological characteristics that may provide an advantage for competitors in each event or position and that may therefore be used as selection parameters in programs to identify talented young athletes

To achieve these objectives, we analyzed the data that focused on absolute size, somatotype, relative size or proportionality, and body composition. The results of our analyses were reported in chapters 3 through 6. Because of the many comparisons performed, the likelihood of achieving significance by chance alone was increased. So in this summary chapter we will attempt to look for overall trends, with supporting evidence from all four chapters, and to relate these findings to our current knowledge of some of the biomechanical and physiological requirements for success in each sport and event.

Summaries of the average characteristics for each sport are given for male competitors in Table 7.1 and for female competitors in Table 7.2. Although there are differences by event, place, or playing position within sports, the group means present an overall picture of the findings for each sport. However, because of large differences between long-distance and other swimmers, they are separated into two groups for these tables.

Swimming

Swimmers who competed in more than one event at the World Championships designated their best three events as first, second, and third preferences. Differences in morphology were sought between swimmers in the four strokes as well as between those competing over a variety of distances. In this chapter, 50 m and 100 m events for each stroke are referred to as short distance (SD), whereas 200 m and 400 m events are called middle distance (MD). The 800 m (female swimmers) and 1500 m (male swimmers) are both labeled middle-to-long distance (ML). The 25 km open water swim is long distance (LD). The swimming strokes are abbreviated as FR (freestyle), BR (breaststroke), BK (backstroke), FL (butterfly), and IM (individual medley). Swimmers who finished in the top 12 places for each stroke were categorized as Best and were compared to others of lower rank denoted Rest.

To facilitate the interpretation of the results from previous chapters we have identified a theoretical model of performance to which we relate significant findings. The model proposed by Grimston and Hay (1986) focuses on the relationships between stroking speed and anthropometric characteristics. Using this model, Grimston and Hay sought to elucidate the relationship of 21 anthropometric parameters, which included segment lengths and areas in cross-section, with average stroking speed, average stroke length, and average stroke frequency as dependent variables. Only 12 male college-level swimmers were used in their analysis, yet sigificant relationships were reported for several anthropometric variables with stroke length and frequency. In particular, the cross-sectional area of the hand and transverse sectional area of the trunk at the level of the axilla, together with foot, arm, and leg lengths, were significantly related to these performance parameters.

Average stroke length, according to Changalur and Brown (1992), is the single most important factor affecting the final time achieved among 200 m FR, BR, and FL. Data were collected during competition at the 1988 Seoul Olympics, and significant correlations of between −0.34 and −0.63 were reported for average

Table 7.1   Means for Age and Structural Characteristics of Male Athletes

Variable	Swimmers	Long-distance swimmers	Divers	Water polo players
N	218	13	43	190
Age (yr)	21.3	21.8	22.2	25.3
Stature (cm)	184.0	179.6	170.9	186.5
Body mass (kg)	78.4	78.1	66.7	86.1
Proportional mass (kg)	62.0	66.4	65.9	65.4
Endomorphy	1.9	2.5	2.0	2.5
Mesomorphy	5.0	5.3	5.3	5.3
Ectomorphy	2.9	2.3	2.4	2.4
SUM6SF (mm)	44.9	60.3	44.6	62.5
Relative muscle mass (%)	57.9	56.3	58.5	56.0
Relative skeletal mass (%)	13.1	13.0	13.0	12.8
Muscle: skeleton	4.4	4.3	4.6	4.4

Table 7.2   Means for Age and Structural Characteristics of Female Athletes

Variable	Swimmers	Long-distance swimmers	Divers	Synchronized swimmers	Water polo players
N	160	10	39	137	109
Age (yr)	19.3	22.8	20.9	20.4	23.7
Stature (cm)	172.1	162.6	161.2	166.0	171.3
Body mass (kg)	63.2	62.2	53.7	56.7	64.8
Proportional mass (kg)	61.1	71.3	63.2	61.1	63.5
Endomorphy	2.8	4.4	2.8	3.3	3.6
Mesomorphy	3.8	4.7	3.8	3.5	4.0
Ectomorphy	3.1	1.7	2.8	3.1	2.8
SUM6SF (mm)	70.6	104.6	65.6	81.4	89.8
Relative muscle mass (%)	51.5	46.0	51.9	48.8	49.3
Relative skeletal mass (%)	12.6	11.4	12.2	12.5	12.3
Muscle: skeleton	4.1	4.0	4.3	3.9	4.0

stroke length and final time. Average stroke rate was not significantly related to final time for most event comparisons.

The theoretical model proposed by Grimston and Hay (1986) shows that the swimmer's morphology influences the horizontal components of lift and drag and thereby affects the generation of both propulsion and resistance forces by the swimmer. A balance in body size and shape is therefore required within each stroke if swimmers are to maximize propulsive forces, yet minimize resistance. The differences between stroke and event comparisons (summarized next) may represent morphological compromises that optimize stroking speed.

Differences by Swimming Stroke

The mean male somatotype, 2-5-3 (an ectomesomorph), does not differ between the strokes. Similarly, swimmers of like distance show no differences in body composition. These results are duplicated for female swimmers whose mean somatotype is 3-4-3 (a central type with a slight mesomorphic dominance).

Most stroke differences in the short-distance events appear in the absolute and relative size variables, particularly between FR and BR or FL. Few differences are noted between FR and BK, which reflects the similarity in the general mechanics of these two strokes. Indeed, the better male FR and BK performers are typically taller, with longer upper and lower limbs than the Rest. These traits are confirmed also for proportionality differences and in body composition, where the Best FR possess a smaller muscle:skeletal mass ratio than the Rest.

Male FR are taller though relatively lighter than BR and FL, with longer lower limbs. As a consequence, compared to FR, FL are proportionally heavier and larger in four breadths, 10 girths, and six skinfold thicknesses (SUM6SF). It is interesting, however, that the best FL are taller, with a longer trunk and smaller proportional skinfolds compared to the rest.

Male BR are also proportionally heavier than FR and proportionally larger in biacromial breadth, AP chest depth, and in four-segment girths. These more robust characteristics, advantageous for BR, give the Best swimmers a larger absolute size in eight girths and four breadths. Like FL, the Best BR compared to the Rest are also the tallest individuals, with higher means on eight upper and lower limb lengths and a higher relative skeletal mass. It is noteworthy that male BR possess relatively longer feet than FR, a trait also seen in female BR.

Although female FR do not display the same dominance as male FR in stature over the other strokes, they do possess longer upper and lower limbs than BR and FL without differing from BK. The better FR and BK also possess longer limb segments than the rest, however the average female BK is less robust than FR, being proportionally lighter and smaller in AP chest depth and in five girths.

In general, female FL are proportionally smaller than FR for many segment lengths. Yet the Best swimmers are those of greatest stature, with larger values on six breadths, but with relatively less fat as indicated at six skinfold sites. The Best FL have lower SUM6SF and possess greater relative muscle mass than the Rest. Alternatively, BR, a relatively homogeneous group apart from size difference compared to FR, show few differences between Best and Rest competitors.

IM generally excel in more than one stroke and consequently should not possess extreme body morphology. No differences were noted between IM and those in the single strokes. Male IM are very homogeneous in size with few differences reported between Best and Rest competitors; for females, the better swimmers are leaner and less robust than the Rest.

Three important features are revealed when seeking common traits among the Best swimmers in these short-distance events. Despite the mean differences for segment lengths between strokes, the Best swimmers possess longer absolute limb lengths, especially foot length. With respect to the model of performance by Grimston and Hay (1986), the beneficial effects of longer body segments among sprint swimmers would appear to influence the development of propulsive forces to a greater extent than resistance forces.

The Best SD and MD are also generally taller than the Rest. Support for these results can be seen also from studies reporting on active drag in swimmers (Huijing et al., 1988; Toussaint, de Looze, van Rossem, Leijdekkers, & Dignum, 1990). In adult swimmers, Huijing et al. have shown a high correlation between active drag and the cross-sectional area of the body exposed to water flow. However, when increases in cross-sectional area are combined with increased stature (Toussaint et al.), active drag remains relatively unchanged for velocities of between 0.8 and 1.5 m/s. It was suggested by Toussaint et al. that increases in stature and the associated decrease in Froude number, serves to reduce wave-making resistance. This presumably would counter the increased pressure drag caused by any increase in cross-sectional area, making negligible the net effect on total active drag. No difference in stature between Best and Rest swimmers was found for ML. Finally, in almost all strokes, the Best performers have lower proportional skinfold thicknesses.

Differences by Event Distance

FR were compared across the greatest range of distances, from 50 m to 25 km. Although few differences are revealed for events below 800 m in body lengths, there are significant size, somatotype, and composition differences for ML and LD compared to SD and MD. Male and female LD are more endomorphic and mesomorphic but less ectomorphic than all other FR, with mean somatotypes of 2.5-5.3-2.3 and 1.8-4.5-3.2, respectively for males; 4.4-4.7-1.7 and 2.8-3.7-3.2, respectively, for females.

The higher endomorphy is supported by greater SUM6SF in LD than other groups for both male and female swimmers, as well as higher proportional skinfolds at all eight sites compared to SD. This dominance in body fat so influences the composition of female LD that they possess a smaller relative muscle mass than SD, MD, and ML, despite a greater mesomorphy rating for LD. Although the number of LD was too small to permit a valid analysis by performance rank, the proportionality results show that the Best female LD have lower proportional weight and skinfold thicknesses than the rest. Therefore increased adiposity may provide some buoyancy and insulation advantage for LD. However, the higher levels of subcutaneous fat (maximum SUM6SF = 80.8 mm for males; 147.1 mm for females) do not appear to assist performance, as these competitors were not among the Best.

Differences in mesomorphy and ectomorphy are cited in chapters 3 and 5 for both males and females, wherein SD are taller than LD and have longer upper and lower limb dimensions. Despite smaller absolute size values for some girths and breadths, LD are proportionally heavier and larger on most breadths and on all 11 girths compared to SD and MD.

ML tend to be less robust than SD and MD especially among the males, with the former having significantly lower values on three absolute girth measurements. In addition, ML have proportionally smaller neck, arm, and thigh girths, as well as lower values on two skinfolds than SD. Furthermore, the Best male and female ML are longer in the trunk than the Rest. These morphological characteristics, reflected in lower values for segment frontal areas, affect the coefficients of lift and drag. The combined effect may result in sacrificing generation of some propulsive force in favor of significant reductions in drag force. Thus, if economy of motion is the overriding strategy for success in ML events, these modifications to swimmers' size and shape appear to serve adequately.

MD seldom differed from SD apart from higher proportional skinfold thicknesses at seven sites among the male MD, and indeed the better performers show characteristics similar to the best male and female SD. That is, they are taller and heavier with longer upper and lower limbs and greater chest and shoulder dimensions than the rest.

For strokes other than FR, 200 m swimmers were compared to their sprint counterparts (50 m and 100 m) in chapters 4, 5, and 6. Among BR, male 200 m swimmers are more robust, with proportionally higher values for weight, three breadths, and four girths. Few differences are noted for female BR. By contrast, male BK competing in the 200 m event are proportionally lighter with smaller breadths and girths compared to the sprinters. There are no differences for male FL; however, the female 200 m swimmers have proportionally bigger breadths, girths, and skinfolds than sprinters.

Diving

Divers competed in one or more 1M, 3M, or 10M (platform) events at the World Championships, and differences between performers who specialized or excelled in these events were examined. Among female competitors, we noted few differences between 1M and 3M performers; however, 10 M specialists possess less massive physiques. In absolute terms, 10M performers have a smaller upper thigh girth and transverse chest breadth, whereas they are proportionally smaller in eight girths, two breadths, and sitting height, but longer in thigh and leg lengths, besides having a smaller proportional weight. No differences were noted in somatotype ($\overline{S}$ = 3-4-3) or body composition between events.

Few differences were reported between events for male divers especially in absolute size, body composition, and rounded somatotype ($\overline{S}$ = 2-5$^1/_2$-2$^1/_2$). The 10M divers are, however, proportionally smaller in four girths and both transverse and AP chest breadths, which would indicate a less massive physique than 1M specialists. Because the main elements of somersaulting, twisting, flight path, and body position are common to each of the diving events, it is logical to find performers fairly homogeneous in morphology. Perhaps the elements of performance during the flight phase and entry are more critical in the 10M event, whereby a less massive body type could be advantageous. Decreased moments of inertia are afforded by smaller absolute and proportional limb girths and segment breadths, and these may provide an advantage for 10M specialists in aerial maneuvers.

Divers who placed among the top 10 in any event were compared to the rest of the competitors. Few differences are reported for the better female performers in absolute terms; however, they tend to be leaner (smaller SUM6SF), have smaller proportional weight, and are proportionally smaller in three lengths, two breadths, and four girths. Once again, this body size and shape may provide an advantage to the diver in the performance of aerial maneuvers. The better male divers tend to be leaner than the Rest; however, few other differences were apparent, suggesting a male group very homogeneous in morphology.

Synchronized Swimming

SS competed in one or more of the solo, duet, and team events at the World Championships, and differences between swimmers who preferred or excelled in each of these events were examined. A wide range of somatotypes are found for all SS, however they cluster around a mean of $3^1/2$-$3^1/2$-3 (a central type). No differences in mean somatotypes are found between events nor in body composition variables. Soloists were generally leaner than team competitors, although this finding did not reach significance. However, when the skinfolds are proportionally adjusted for stature, soloists have lower thicknesses at five skinfold sites.

There are no differences for absolute size variables between solo and duet performers; however, soloists are significantly taller and possess longer upper and lower limbs compared to team SS. This more linear morphology is supported by the proportionality analysis wherein soloists have a smaller proportional weight as well as smaller proportional values for two breadths and nine girths compared to team SS. Furthermore, the soloists had higher proportional arm, thigh, and foot lengths.

We suggested in chapter 3 that these characteristics of body morphology may be advantageous for the soloist not only for aesthetic reasons, but also for their ability to execute figures and strokes with technical excellence. Francis and Welshons-Smith (1982) reported that a combination of both lift and drag forces are required by the arm action during the single leg support scull. Longer limb segments, both in absolute and proportional dimensions combined with proportionally smaller segment girths, would therefore assist the solo SS in the development of lift forces using the ''egg-beater'' kick and in sustained support sculling.

However, results from the analysis of Best performers versus Rest suggest that for solo and duet SS proportionally long forearms and thighs are contraindicated. Perhaps SS with very long limbs do not possess the muscular strength and power to use these long levers effectively. Even so, the Best performers do possess proportionaly longer arm span and foot length.

An optimal combination of lever length, muscular strength, and a reduction in excess mass (due to less body fat) should assist the SS to better perform the dynamic sections of the routine. Although no differences are shown between

Best and Rest in absolute levels of body fat, the analysis in chapter 5 showed that the best team SS have significantly lower proportional thickness at seven skinfold sites.

Water Polo

WP designated their primary playing position as center forward (CF), center back (CB), goalkeeper (GK), or offensive and defensive wing, denoted as other positions (OTH). Differences in morphology were sought between players in these positions. The rounded mean somatotype for all male WP is $2^1/_2$-$5^1/_2$-$2^1/_2$ (a balanced mesomorph). Only ectomorphy is different between positions, where GK are significantly more ectomorphic than CF. CB and OTH are similar in somatotype to CF.

Although similar in somatotype to CF and CB, OTH are significantly smaller and lighter, being smaller in body mass, stature, and four segment lengths, 13 girths, and seven breadths. CF and, to a lesser extent, CB are therefore the largest and most robust of all players. CF have a significantly higher proportional weight compared to OTH, possibly due to higher proportional skinfold thicknesses and waist girth. These differences were not denoted in chapter 6 because the SUM6SF was not dimensionally scaled to a common stature. Clearly, however, CF possess higher levels of skinfolds in proportion to their size than OTH. The advantage of greater size for CF enhances their ability to provide a large focal point for the team when attacking the opponent's goal, as well as a protection from constant physical contact by the CB.

GK are similar to OTH on most girth and breadth dimensions but are more like CF and CB in stature and individual segment lengths. This more ectomorphic characteristic of GK is supported by the higher relative skeletal mass compared to CF. Similarly, GK have significantly lower proportional weight compared to OTH. Apparently due to lower proportional girth measures (especially in the upper body), this attribute indicates reduced upper limb inertia, which would facilitate relatively quick movement to protect the goal.

The mean somatotype for all female WP is rounded $3^1/_2$-4-3 (a central type). The results for players by position mirrored that for males, with OTH being significantly smaller and lighter than CF and CB. These differences are shown in many absolute and proportional size variables. CF in particular have greater proportional weight, due to greater musculature (higher absolute and proportional breadths and girths) and greater adiposity (higher proportional skinfold thicknesses).

Like their male counterparts, female GK are more ectomorphic than players in all other positions, with similar absolute girth and breadth values to OTH, but they have linear dimensions more akin to CF and CB. GK also have lower proportional weight and lower proportional values for five breadths and six girths compared to OTH. These results confirm the upper-body movement advantage afforded GK by this specific body morphology.

WP teams were also categorized in terms of final placement: Players from the finals (Best) teams were compared with team members who finished in the lowest order (Rest). Using these groupings, we noted few differences between Best and Rest male and female WP in somatotype, absolute size, or body composition variables. Because of the large variation in body size and shape for positional players on each team, the lack of differences is not unexpected. In future research it may be more useful to partition the team into respective player positions before running this analysis.

Male WP in the Best teams have a smaller proportional weight than the Rest, explained by lower proportional values for two lengths, two breadths, five girths, and two skinfold thicknesses. A similar trend is shown for the females who have lower proportional values for hip and thigh girths and two skinfolds. Even though WP are among the largest of aquatic athletes, and a certain body size and structure is required for success in the sport, these results reinforce the notion that body morphology alone is not the key to success. Clearly, the biggest players did not ensure team success.

Concluding Remarks

This monograph provides a preliminary kinanthropometric description and analysis of data collected on athletes at the World Championships in swimming, diving, synchronized swimming, and water polo in Perth, 1991. Within the constraints of space we have provided the basic information on absolute and relative size, somatotype, and body composition of athletes in the four sports by gender, event or playing position, and performance level. Although physique is only one of several aspects of successful physical performance, it is nonetheless a very important foundation upon which success is built. We hope that the kinanthropometric prototypes we have presented will both provide a better understanding of the relationships between structure and function in elite athletes and set the stage for further studies and analysis.

Appendix A

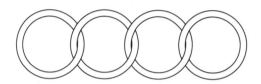

Data Sheets and Reports

A.1   Letter of invitation to participate in KASP.

A.2   Data recording sheet (two sides): aims and methods, statement of consent, demographic information, items measured, and data record.

A.3   Individual report summary for a male swimmer, ID #524 from Canada, compared to male swimmers from the 1976 Olympics.

A.4   Individual somatoplot of swimmer #524 compared to the mean and distribution of a combined sample of male Olympic swimmers from 1968 and 1976 Olympics.

A.5   Group report of all male swimmers compared to male swimmers at the 1976 Olympics.

The University of Western Australia

KASP (a FINA approved project)

**Department of Human Movement
and Recreation Studies**
Nedlands, Perth, Western Australia 6009
Facsimile (09) 380 1039, Telex AA92992
Telephone (09) 380 2361

October 29, 1990

Dear

It is my pleasure to invite members of your team to participate in the Kinanthropometric Aquatic Sports Project (KASP) which will be conducted just prior to the World Championships in Perth at the end of the year. This project is endorsed by FINA and the Australian Swimming, Diving, Water Polo, and Synchronized Swimming Federations.

I have enclosed copies of a brochure for distribution among your team members so that they may also understand the tests and benefits of this study. The scientific committee, who will administer this project, consists of the world renown researchers in the field with a wealth of experience in similar projects (for example, The Montreal Olympic Games Anthropological Project). We are therefore sympathetic to the coaches' desires that no adverse influence be imposed on athletes prior to competition. Thus, no information or feedback will be given directly to the athlete but instead, via the team coach or manager.

Details of the benefits of this project may be seen in both the brochure and the attached project summary. If you have any questions please do not hesitate to contact me by telephone or fax.

Meantime I would be pleased if you could return to me the confirmation slip (yellow) by **AIRMAIL** or **FAX**. You would note that three alternative testing venues will be provided and we ask that you indicate your preferences.

a) At the Championship Venue: Testing will be organised in conjunction with rostered training times in the competition pools. A close liason between KASP directors and Championship organisers will ensure a smooth operation.

b) At the University of Western Australia laboratory: This is located adjacent to the residential colleges in which many teams will be accommodated. It is possible that teams choosing this venue will have access to an adjacent heated pool for a concurrent training session.

c) At your accommodation venue: Several larger teams will be accommodated in large hotels, and it may be possible to set up a small laboratory to measure the entire team on a single occasion.

All measurements will be standard, non-invasive anthropometric tests and each athlete will be required to attend the laboratory for only about 1 hr. I look forward to your reply and to meeting you in Perth in December this year.

Yours sincerely,

Tim Ackland Ph.D.
KASP Managing Director

Figure A.1   Letter of invitation to participate in KASP.

KINANTHROPOMETRIC AQUATIC SPORTS PROJECT

INVESTIGATORS

Dr. T.R. Ackland	The University of Western Australia
Dr. J.C. Mazza	Biosystem, Rosario, Argentina
Dr. J.E.L. Carter	San Diego State University, USA
Dr. W.D. Ross	Simon Fraser University, Canada

Aims and Methods of Study

The purpose of the project is to examine the relationships between physique and performance in four aquatic sports (swimming, diving, synchronised swimming and water polo) using athletes of international calibre. Only limited data pertaining to physique for diving, synchronised swimming and water polo exists, and with great changes in the training and preparation of swimmers over the last two decades, existing swimming data is likely out of date and of limited value.

In the current project, athletes from each of the four sports will be measured in the period surrounding the VIth World Championships of Swimming, Diving, Synchronised Swimming, and Water Polo. Approximately 40 body dimensions will be measured and each subject will be photographed to provide somatotype data (describing the relative linearity, muscularity and fatness of the athlete). In addition, basic demographic data will be recorded, along with menarche information from female athletes. None of the measurements are expected to cause any discomfort.

One testing session will be required and this will be conducted at the site of the Championships, at the University of Western Australia or your accommodation venue. The session is expected to last approximately one hour.

All athletes will receive a report describing their individual physique profile, together with data describing mean values for athletes of similar event and gender. A follow-up report will present group and average data of all competitors in the Championships.

Any questions concerning this study can be directed to Dr. Tim Ackland of the Deparment of Human Movement and Recreation Studies, at the University of Western Australia.

Statement of Consent

I have been asked to participate in the above research study after having my rights and obligations explained to my satisfaction and give my consent by signing this form on the understanding that:

1. All costs associated with this project will be carried out at no cost to myself.
2. In giving my consent I acknowledge that my participation in this research is voluntary, that I may withdraw at any time, and that I may be asked by the investigators to withdraw at any time.
3. I agree that research data gathered for the study may be published provided that my name is not used.

_____   _____
Participant   Investigator

_____
Date

(continued)

Figure A.2   Data recording sheet (two sides): aims and methods, statement of consent, demographic information, items measured, and data record.

KASP Demographic Information

1. Name of subject: _____
   (last or family name)   (first)

2. Address: _____

   _____

   _____ Phone: _____

4. Place of Birth: _____ Country: _____

5. Family size (number of brothers and sisters including self) ☐

6. Birth order (position in family) ☐

7. Number of school years completed ☐

8. What is your present occupation: _____ ☐

9. Ethnic/racial background: _____ ☐

White Caucasian	1	Mestizo-Latin American	6
Black Negroid:		Oriental Mongoloid	7
African	2	Middle Eastern	8
North American	3	Indian subcontinent	9
South/Central American	4	other/uncertain	0
Caribbean	5		

10. For females only:
    Estimated month and year of first menstrual flow _____ 19 _____ ☐

    Indicate accuracy of recall using numbers 0 to 5

not yet	0	approximate	3
certain	1	uncertain	4
fairly certain	2	unwilling to respond	5

11. Remarks: _____

    _____

    _____

    _____

    Signature of Interviewer: _____

Figure A.2 (*continued*)

Kinanthropometric Aquatic Sports Project

Subject name (last, first) _____, _____ Subject ID# [   ]

Sport ID# [ ]   Events (1°, 2°, 3°) [ ]1° [ ]2° [ ]3°

Country [   ]   Ethnicity [ ]   Sex (2=F, 1=M) [ ]   Projection box + constant [|]

Date of birth Year Month Day [ ][ ][ ]

Date of measurement Year Month Day [ ][ ][ ]   Checker ID# [ ]

Triceps sf								
Subscapular sf								
Biceps sf								
Iliac crest sf								
Supraspinale sf								
Abdominal sf								
Front thigh sf								
Medial calf sf								
Acromiale-radiale								
Radiale-stylion								
Midstylion-dactylion								
Iliospinale b.ht								
Trochanterion b.ht								
Trochanterion-tibiale laterale								
Tibiale laterale ht								
Tibiale mediale-sphyrion tibiale								
Arm girth relaxed								
Arm girth fully flexed and tensed								
Forearm girth maximum								
Wrist girth distal styloids								
Chest girth mesosternale								
Waist girth minimum								
Hip (gluteal) girth								
Thigh girth (1) 1 cm gluteal line								
Thigh girth (2) mid tro-tib lat								
Calf girth maximum								
Ankle girth minimum								

Figure A.2   (*continued*)

Kinanthropometric Aquatic Sports Project *(continued)*

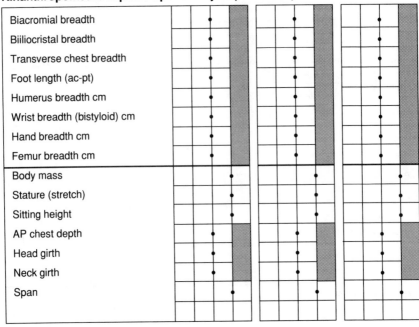

Biacromial breadth

Biiliocristal breadth

Transverse chest breadth

Foot length (ac-pt)

Humerus breadth cm

Wrist breadth (bistyloid) cm

Hand breadth cm

Femur breadth cm

Body mass

Stature (stretch)

Sitting height

AP chest depth

Head girth

Neck girth

Span

Figure A.2   *(continued)*

Kinanthropometric Aquatic Sports Project (KASP)
Sixth World Aquatics Championships, Perth, Australia, 1991

Subject name XXX   Measurements compared to
Subject ID# 524   male swimmers, 1976 Olympics
Sex .... Male
Country (sport) .... Can (swimming)

	Measured	Ref. mean	0-10%	10-25%	25-45%	45-55%	55-75%	75-90%	90-100
Age	25.9	19.3							X
Body mass	86.4	73.0							X
Stature	178.7	178.6			X				
Skinfolds									
Triceps	8.6	7.4						X	
Subscapular	7.9	8.1					X		
Biceps	3.5	n/a							
Iliac crest	10.2	n/a							
Supraspinale	6.8	6.0					X		
Abdominal	10.7	9.0						X	
Front thigh	14.7	9.6							X
Medial calf	7.3	7.2					X		
SUM4SF	30.5	28.7					X		
Sum6SF	55.9	47.2						X	
Girths									
Head	56.7	n/a							
Neck	40.0	n/a							
Arm (relaxed)	35.7	30.6							X
Arm (flexed and tensed)	37.8	33.3							X
Forearm (maximum)	29.6	27.4						X	
Wrist (distal styloid)	18.1	17.1						X	
Chest (mesosternale)	113.5	98.6							X
Waist (minimum)	90.4	79.3							X
Hip (gluteal)	96.7	n/a							
Upper-thigh	63.3	55.4							X
Midthigh	57.4	n/a							
Calf (maximum)	38.0	36.9					X		
Ankle (minimum)	22.7	n/a							
Breadths/Depths									
Biacromial	41.9	40.8					X		
Transverse chest	31.5	29.4							X
AP chest depth	20.5	20.7				X			
Biiliocristal	28.8	27.9					X		
Humerus (biepicondylar)	7.6	7.3						X	
Wrist	6.0	n/a							
Femur (bicondylar)	9.6	9.8				X			

(continued)

Figure A.3   Individual report summary for a male swimmer, ID #524 from Canada compared to male swimmers from the 1976 Olympics.

	Measured	Ref. mean	0-10%	10-25%	25-45%	45-55%	55-75%	75-90%	90-100
Direct and derived lengths									
Sitting height..............................	96.5	94.5						X	
Upper limb-hand......................	63.8	60.3							X
Upper arm.................................	36.1	34.5						X	
Forearm.....................................	27.5	25.7							X
Hand..	20.8	20.0						X	
Lower limb................................	87.2	84.1						X	
Thigh...	38.1	37.0					X		
Leg..	49.1	47.1					X		
Foot length................................	27.4	26.8					X		
Somatotype (Heath-Carter)									
Endomorphy (height corrected)	1.9	2.1			X				
Mesomorphy	5.0	5.1				X			
Ectomorphy...............................	2.9	2.8						X	

Somatoplot...............................X: 1.0 Y: 5.2

Figure A.2 (*continued*)

Male swimmers

X = Ecto-Endo

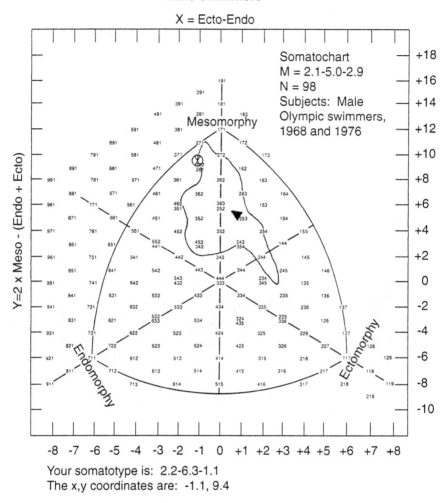

Your somatotype is: 2.2-6.3-1.1
The x,y coordinates are: -1.1, 9.4

Figure A.4   Individual somatoplot of swimmer #524 compared to the mean and distribution of a combined sample of male Olympic swimmers from the 1968 and 1976 Olympics.

Kinanthropometric Aquatic Sports Project (KASP)
Sixth World Aquatics Championships, Perth, Australia, 1991

Subject name XXX   Measurements compared to
Subject ID# 524   male swimmers, 1976 Olympics
Sex .... Male
Country (sport) .... Can (swimming)

	Measured	Ref. mean	0-10%	10-25%	25-45%	45-55%	55-75%	75-90%	90-100
Age	25.9	19.3							X
Body mass	86.4	73.0							X
Stature	178.7	178.6			X				
Skinfolds									
Triceps	8.6	7.4						X	
Subscapular	7.9	8.1					X		
Biceps	3.5	n/a							
Iliac crest	10.2	n/a							
Supraspinale	6.8	6.0					X		
Abdominal	10.7	9.0						X	
Front thigh	14.7	9.6							X
Medial calf	7.3	7.2					X		
SUM4SF	30.5	28.7					X		
Sum6SF	55.9	47.2						X	
Girths									
Head	56.7	n/a							
Neck	40.0	n/a							
Arm (relaxed)	35.7	30.6							X
Arm (flexed and tensed)	37.8	33.3							X
Forearm (maximum)	29.6	27.4						X	
Wrist (distal styloid)	18.1	17.1						X	
Chest (mesosternale)	113.5	98.6							X
Waist (minimum)	90.4	79.3							X
Hip (gluteal)	96.7	n/a							
Upper-thigh	63.3	55.4							X
Midthigh	57.4	n/a							
Calf (maximum)	38.0	36.9					X		
Ankle (minimum)	22.7	n/a							
Breadths/Depths									
Biacromial	41.9	40.8					X		
Transverse chest	31.5	29.4							X
AP chest depth	20.5	20.7			X				
Biiliocristal	28.8	27.9					X		
Humerus (biepicondylar)	7.6	7.3						X	
Wrist	6.0	n/a							
Femur (bicondylar)	9.6	9.8			X				

(*continued*)

Figure A.5   Group report of all male swimmers compared to male swimmers at the 1976 Olympics.

	Measured	Ref. mean	0-10%	10-25%	25-45%	45-55%	55-75%	75-90%	90-100
Direct and derived lengths									
Sitting height	93.3	94.5			X				
Upper limb-hand	63.0	60.3						X	
Upper arm	36.2	34.5						X	
Forearm	26.8	25.7						X	
Hand	19.8	20.0				X			
Lower limb	85.4	84.1					X		
Thigh	36.6	37.0			X				
Leg	48.8	47.1					X		
Foot length	26.4	26.8			X				
Somatotype (Heath-Carter)									
Endomorphy (height corrected)	2.2	2.1				X			
Mesomorphy	6.3	5.1							X
Ectomorphy	1.1	2.8	X						

Somatoplot .... X: −1.1 Y: 9.4

Figure A.5 (*continued*)

Appendix B

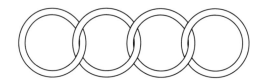

Anthropometric Techniques: Precision and Accuracy

William D. Ross, Deborah A. Kerr, J.E. Lindsay Carter, Timothy R. Ackland, and Timothy M. Bach

This appendix describes and cites pertinent references for the procedures used to assure both precision and accuracy of measurement in the Kinanthropometric Aquatic Sports Project (KASP).

Precision is the consistency of replicated measures. Accuracy is the agreement of measured scores with their "true values" and presupposes precision. The overall quality of measurement depends on adherence to the specified protocol, instrument selection and manipulation, landmark identification, the training of anthropometrists, and the efficiency of data management.

The order and sequence of assembling data are essential features of the anthropometric style, as discussed by Ross, De Rose, and Ward (1988) and in detail more recently by Ross and Marfell-Jones (1991). Style involves more than the specification of the measurement and description of the technique. It also involves personal discipline and commitment, consistency in the manipulation of instruments, skill in the positioning of subjects, surety of touch in marking and measuring, and meticulousness in reading and recording.

The KASP "proforma," or data sheet, with groups of measures and their replication fit into a one-page form that had demographic information on the reverse side (see Appendix A.2). In addition to demographic information, 42 anthropometric dimensions were taken, including body mass, stature, arm span, 8 skinfolds, 10 lengths or heights, 13 girths, and 8 breadths.

Instruments

The instruments used at the Superdrome laboratory in Perth included a Harpenden stadiometer, Harpenden skinfold calipers, steel metric anthropometric tapes (Lufkin W606 PM 2 m), wide-spreading calipers (Siber Hegner GPM), adapted Mitutoyo small-bone calipers, a 30 × 40 × 50-cm measuring box, a Seca beam-type weighing scale, and a marked paper scale attached to a wall for obtaining arm span. Field sites had a portable stadiometer for stature and sitting height and a portable beam-type weighing scale.

Criticism of projected measurements using anthropometers by Day (1984, 1986) spawned a series of studies at Simon Fraser University and resulted in the development of an adapted retractable metal tape (Lufkin, #Y23CM). Called a *segmometer*, it measures both direct lengths and selected projected heights, the latter made to marked sites on the subject from a measuring box. Preliminary studies showed that this new instrument yielded technical errors of measurement as low or lower than those obtained from projected heights from the floor using an anthropometer. In both the laboratory and at field sites, five direct lengths and three projected heights were measured using a segmometer that was adapted from the Simon Fraser prototype (Carr, Blade, Rempel, & Ross, 1993) which used plastic pointers as illustrated in Figure B.1.

Figure B.1   The segmometer as used in KASP. A retractable metal tape (Lufkin, #Y23CM), showing the plastic branches mounted to form the end pointer (left) and housing pointer (right). This device was used to measure direct lengths and projected heights.

Techniques and Landmarks

Descriptions and techniques were based on conventions, anatomical descriptions, and the classical landmarks specified by Martin and Saller (1957). They are similar to those used in studies of Olympic athletes by de Garay et al. (1974) and Carter (1982a) and were recently described by Ross and Marfell-Jones (1991). Although some of the items are similar, many differ from those specified by Hrdlicka (1952), Weiner and Lourie (1981), and Lohman, Roche, and Martorell (1988).

The following sites were marked as described by Ross and Marfell-Jones (1991): acromiale, radiale, stylion, mesosternale, iliospinale, trochanterion, tibiale laterale, and midacromiale-radiale (used to mark arm girth, triceps, and biceps skinfold sites). The adapted KASP protocol for direct hand length, midthigh girth, and tibiale length required additional markings: midstylion ulnare-radiale distance on the anterior surface of the wrist, midtrochanterion-tibiale distance, tibiale mediale, and sphyrion tibiale sites. These and other classical landmarks used in marking subjects are shown in Figure B.2.

All techniques used in KASP are described in Ross and Marfell-Jones (1991) except for eight direct or projected lengths, midthigh girth, wrist and hand breadth, and arm span, which are defined and described in the following paragraphs.

During direct measures of the arm and forearm, the subject stood erect with arms at the sides, palms against the thighs. The segmometer housing was held in the anthropometrist's (measurer's) right hand by an overgrasp of the fingers. The pointer end was grapsed by the left index finger and thumb. In the direct length technique, the proximal landmark was located by the index finger, which anchored and stabilized the skin surface while the pointer was applied to the marked site. The measurer then extended the tape with the right hand and applied the housing pointer to the marked distal site.

Acromiale-Radiale Length (arm length)

Distance from the acromiale to the radiale. The subject stood erect with arms extended downward and palms pressed against the side of the thigh. The anthropometrist anchored the end pointer to the acromiale and placed the housing pointer on the radiale as shown in Figure B.3.

Radiale-Stylion Length (forearm length)

Distance from the radiale to the stylion. The subject stood as described in the previous procedure. The end pointer of the segmometer was placed on the radiale and the housing pointer on the stylion, orienting the tape to parallel the long axis of the radius.

Midstylion-Dactylion Length (hand length)

The shortest distance from the marked midstylion line to dactylion 3. The subject presented his or her right wrist with the hand supinated (palms up) and the fingers

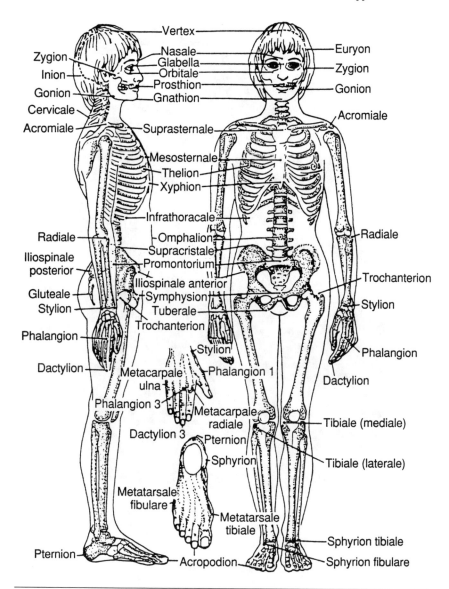

Figure B.2   Classical anthropometric landmarks used in marking sites, describing measurements, and training programs.
From "Anthropometric Concomitants of X-Chromosome Aneuploidies" by W.D. Ross, R. Ward, B.A. Sigmon, and R.M. Leahy. In the *The Cytogenetics of the Mammalian X-Chromosome* by A.V. Sandberg (Ed.), 1983, New York: Alan R. Liss, Inc. Copyright 1983 by Alan R. Liss, Inc. Reprinted by permission of Wiley-Liss.

fully extended. The end pointer of the segmometer was placed on the marked midstylion line, the housing pointer was held in the measurer's right hand and applied to the most distal point of the third digit.

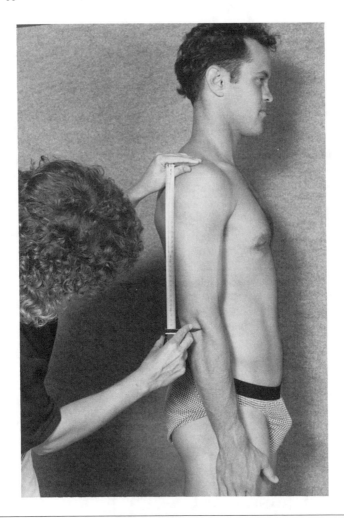

Figure B.3   Direct arm length measurement is taken, acromiale to radiale, using the segmometer.

Iliospinale Height

Projected height from the box to the iliospinale. The subject stood with feet together facing the box (toes underneath in a cutout portion). The end pointer of the segmometer was placed flush on the box and extending the housing pointer vertically upward to the marked iliospinale site.

Trochanterion Height

Projected height from the box to the trochanterion. The subject stood with feet together and the lateral aspect of the right leg against the box. The end pointer

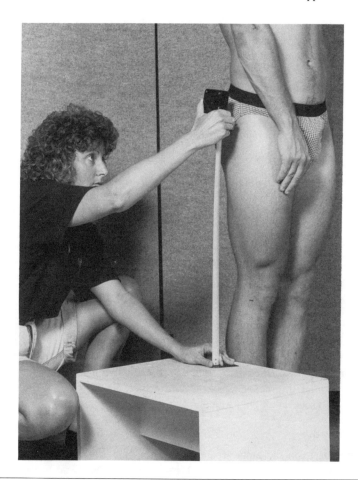

Figure B.4   Trochanterion height is taken projected from a box of known height using the segmometer.

was placed flush against the box and the housing pointer was extended vertically upward to the marked trochanterion site (Figure B.4).

Trochanterion-Tibiale Laterale Length (thigh 2 length)

Distance from the trochanterion to the tibiale laterale. The subject stood with feet together on the box with his or her right side toward the anthropometrist. The end pointer was placed on the marked trochanterion and the housing pointer was extended with the measurer's right hand to the marked tibiale laterale site.

Tibiale Laterale Height

Projected height from the measuring box to the tibiale laterale. The subject stood on the box while the end pointer of the segmometer was placed flush on the box top, and the housing pointer was extended vertically upward with the measurer's right hand to the marked tibiale laterale site.

Tibiale Mediale-Sphyrion Tibiale Length (leg 2 length)

Direct length from tibiale mediale to sphyrion tibiale. The subject sat on the box, crossing the right leg over the left thigh to present a horizontal medial aspect of the leg to the measurer. The end pointer was applied to the marked tibiale mediale site, then the housing pointer was extended to the marked sphyrion tibiale.

Midthigh Girth

Perimeter of the right thigh perpendicular to the long axis of the femur at midtrochanterion-tibiale level. The mid (or middle) thigh girth was obtained by the same technique for thigh girth (taken 1 cm below the gluteal fold) described by Ross and Marfell-Jones (1991). The tape housing was held by the measurer in the right hand, using the third digit of each hand to help anchor and level the tape. The thumb and index fingers controlled the tension and aligned the tape, assuring that the girth was obtained without distorting the skin surface.

Wrist Breadth

Bistyloid wrist breadth when the right forearm rests on the seated subject's thigh and the hand was flexed at the wrist to angle of about 90°. The subject's styloids were palpated by the measurer's third digits, beginning proximal to the sites. Firm pressure was applied to compress the intervening tissue, but not great enough to alter the radius' position with respect to the ulna. The caliper was applied to bisect the angle formed at the wrist.

Hand Breadth

Distance between the metacarpale laterale and metacarpale mediale when the palm with fingers together was placed firmly (without heavy pressure) on a table. The anthropometrist held the small-bone caliper pointed downwards at a 45° angle and palpated the landmarks with the third fingers then applied the faces of the caliper with pressure sufficient to compress the skin without compressing the bony width.

Arm Span

Distance between the dactylions of the right and left hands when the chest and palms were placed against a wall and the outstretched arms were abducted to the horizontal. The subject faced a wall so that the left or right dactylion was placed against a corner wall and the opposite dactylion was volitionally stretched for maximal span. This measurement was then marked on a paper scale attached to the wall, the distance from corner to the marked line was recorded to the nearest 0.1 cm.

The following terms are used for derived lengths:

- Arm length: acromiale to radiale

- Forearm length: radiale to stylion
- Hand length: midstylion to dactylion
- Upper limb length: arm plus forearm plus hand lengths
- Lower limb 1 length: stature minus sitting height
- Thigh 1 length: lower limb 1 length minus tibiale laterale height
- Thigh 2 length: trochanterion minus tibiale laterale height
- Leg 1 length: tibiale laterale height
- Leg 2 length: tibiale mediale to sphyrion tibiale

Common Protocol and Training

The international members of the anthropometric team were selected for their experience and formal background in international workshops and graduate courses at Simon Fraser University in Canada. Additional personnel from Australia were trained in workshops prior to KASP at the University of Western Australia and in Wollongong. Thus, through training and monitoring by designated criterion anthropometrists at each location, measurement protocol adhered to the defined specifications and systematic error was held to a minimum.

Precision of Measurement

The technical error of measurement is an index of precision indicating that two thirds of the time a measurement should come within ± the value of the technical error of measurement. It was obtained by comparing the anthropometrist's first measure with the replicated measure as follows:

$$\text{TEM} = (\Sigma\ (x_2 - x_1)^2 \ / \ 2n)^{0.5} \tag{1}$$

$$\%\ \text{TEM} = 100\ (\text{TEM}/M_1) \tag{2}$$

where: TEM is the technical error of measurement in absolute values, x_1 and x_2 are replicated measurements; n is the number of replicated pairs; M_1 is mean of the first measurements; % TEM is the percent technical error of measurement.

In general, one expects skinfold measurements to have about a 5% technical error of measurement, breadths slightly greater than 1%, and other measurements slightly less than 1%. Guidelines for tolerances between replicated absolute values have been defined by Borms, Hebbelinck, Carter, Ross, and Lariviere (1979), reproduced with some augmentation of items by Ross and Marfell-Jones (1991). Intra- and intermeasurer errors have been reported in Lohman et al. (1988). In the present study, TEM was calculated by combining measures repeated by several anthropometrists. That is, one measurer did repeated measures of a group of variables on a subject or group of subjects; other measurers did the same for other subjects at a different station or time.

The obtained technical errors of measurement as shown in Table B.1 define the precision level of the anthropometry for a single series on men and women

Table B.1   Means and Standard Deviations for Replicated Measures, Differences Between Means, Absolute and Percent Technical Error of Measurement for 42 Anthropometric Variables

Item	n	X1	S1	X2	S2	diff	TEM[a]	% TEM
Skinfolds								
Triceps	898	10.60	4.43	10.56	4.39	0.04	0.39	3.68
Subscapular	898	9.13	2.86	9.10	2.86	0.03	0.35	3.83
Biceps	898	5.07	2.11	5.04	2.14	0.03	0.39	7.69
Iliac crest	898	10.75	4.59	10.76	4.56	−0.01	0.77	7.16
Supraspinale	897	7.61	2.98	7.62	3.01	−0.01	0.57	7.49
Abdominal	898	12.98	6.25	12.87	6.27	0.11	0.67	5.16
Front thigh	898	15.82	7.23	15.84	7.39	−0.02	0.64	4.04
Medial calf	898	9.59	4.32	9.54	4.30	0.05	0.46	4.80
Lengths								
Acromiale–Radiale	76	33.97	2.66	33.94	2.68	0.03	0.28	0.82
Radiale–Stylion	75	25.90	2.08	25.95	2.13	−0.05	0.35	1.35
Midstylion–Dactylion	75	19.63	1.55	19.63	1.54	0.00	0.24	1.22
Iliospinale + bench height	79	66.75	7.26	66.72	7.18	0.03	0.28	0.42
Trochanterion + bench height	80	61.02	6.48	60.98	6.59	0.04	0.46	0.75
Trochanterion–Tibiale laterale	79	44.64	3.22	44.66	3.24	−0.02	0.40	0.90
Tibiale lateral height	74	46.59	3.70	46.52	3.67	0.07	0.21	0.45
Tibiale mediale–Sphyrion tibiale	79	38.74	3.08	38.72	3.08	0.02	0.20	0.52
Foot	61	25.42	1.68	25.43	1.73	−0.01	0.22	0.86
Girths								
Arm (relaxed)	375	30.27	3.04	30.20	2.99	0.07	0.35	1.16
Arm (flexed)	377	31.98	3.44	32.00	3.46	0.02	0.22	0.69

Forearm	370	26.33	2.54	26.31	2.54	0.02	0.17	0.64
Wrist	370	16.17	1.32	16.17	1.31	0.00	0.16	0.99
Chest	876	97.20	8.91	97.12	8.83	0.08	0.83	0.85
Waist	875	74.65	7.94	74.73	7.88	-0.08	0.59	0.79
Hip	874	94.24	5.24	94.30	5.28	-0.06	0.66	0.70
Thigh (gluteal)	371	55.76	3.48	55.76	3.50	0.00	0.42	0.75
Thigh (mid)	371	51.74	3.38	51.77	3.40	-0.03	0.33	0.64
Calf	369	35.79	2.62	35.82	2.63	-0.03	0.20	0.56
Ankle	369	21.57	1.53	21.58	1.52	-0.01	0.20	0.93
Head	55	55.59	2.11	55.58	2.24	0.01	0.24	0.43
Neck	55	36.05	3.50	36.15	3.59	-0.10	0.35	0.97
Breadths								
Biacromial	62	38.89	2.71	38.95	2.63	-0.06	0.37	0.95
Biiliocristal	61	27.28	1.82	27.30	1.77	-0.02	0.32	1.17
Transverse chest	63	28.31	2.67	28.24	2.58	0.07	0.49	1.73
Humerus	53	6.54	0.66	6.53	0.64	0.01	0.10	1.53
Wrist	51	5.32	0.63	5.36	0.63	-0.04	0.10	1.88
Hand	52	7.81	0.71	7.87	0.71	-0.06	0.22	2.82
Femur	52	9.17	0.89	9.18	0.86	-0.01	0.14	1.53
Other								
Body mass	17	64.05	10.84	64.04	10.83	0.01	0.10	0.16
Stature (stretch)	59	174.53	9.86	174.61	9.88	-0.08	0.22	0.12
Sitting height	56	131.41	5.41	131.60	5.42	-0.19	0.37	0.28
AP chest depth	58	19.20	2.36	19.07	2.29	0.13	0.33	1.72
Arm span	55	179.64	12.86	179.81	12.74	-0.17	0.48	0.27

Note. Skinfolds are in millimeters, body mass in kilograms, all others in centimeters.
[a]TEM = technical error of measurement.

under field study conditions by the international team. The reported TEM is somewhat inflated because the median of three or the mean of two measurements was used for each athlete's data whenever possible.

Generally, one measurement is obtained in surveys because of the objective to obtain mean values and their variation. In studies where individual assessment is in any way at issue, it is prudent to replicate measurements. The recommended procedure takes a three-measurement series and uses the median value for each item. Ward (1988) demonstrated in a triple measurement protocol that the median is more resistant to imposed error than the mean of the closest pair. The mean of three measures is less efficient than the median score because it is prone to intermittent gross error, requires calculation, and has a rounding error. Actual measurements follow closely the theoretical expectation for combining independent error that Beers (1957) and Topping (1962) discussed. If, for example, we measured skinfolds with a technical error of 5%, the use of the mean replication of two measures would reduce this to about 3.5%, reducing replication of the mean of three to 2.9%, with the median somewhat lower at perhaps 2.7%.

Practical considerations limited replication of measures in the KASP. We attempted to obtain double or triple measures of skinfold thickness at all eight sites on each subject and to replicate once or twice on other variables, as time and circumstances permitted. In practice, we almost always took double skinfold measures, but a much smaller number of replications were made for other variables. In addition to the replication plan, which permitted calculation of the technical errors of measurement as indicators of precision, the criterion anthropometrists made visual inspections and occasional replications to control for systematic error (i.e., any deviation from prescribed landmarks and techniques).

The obtained absolute and percent technical errors in Table B.1 were generally within the expected range for good measurement precision. The triceps, subscapular, abdominal, front thigh, and medial calf skinfold errors were near or below the 5% target level; whereas the biceps, iliac crest, and supraspinale skinfolds exceeded this level at 7% to 8%. Absolute TEMs for the biceps (0.4 mm) and supraspinale (0.7 mm) skinfolds are similar to those of other skinfolds, but these are the smallest skinfolds. This suggests that the percent TEM may not be as important for these smaller skinfolds as the absolute TEM. Furthermore, because most of the participants in the project had skinfolds measured three times, the median values used in calculations were substantialy more precise than the table levels indicated that were derived from measurements one and two only.

The errors for segmental and projected lengths obtained with the segmometer were less than 1%, except for the radiale-stylion and midstylion dactylion lengths (forearm and hand lengths). Either the instructions were inadequate or the training time was insufficient for the measurement of forearm and hand length. Considering that only the techniques, not the landmarks, were replicated, the results suggest that techniques for marking and obtaining forearm and hand length need improvement, or that some standard replication plan be used for these measurements.

Except for an inexplicably high percent error for relaxed arm girth (1.2%), all of the girths appeared within acceptable range. Biacromial and biiliocristal breadths were as precise as expected. The transverse chest and AP chest depth, which involved breathing cycles, both had technical errors of 1.7%. Conceivably, new instruments would improve breadth measures. Technical errors of 1.5% for the humerus and femur breadths and 1.9% for wrist breadth reflect the expected precision obtainable without changing the measurement technique or improving instrumentation. Change is clearly needed for hand breadth measurement, which at 2.8% had the highest percent TEM of all the breadths. This measure seems sensitive to excessive pressure that can cause transverse movement in the distal ends of the metacarpals.

One of the advantages of international cooperative research is the opportunity to standardize techniques and assess the intensity and adequacy of anthro-pometrists' selection and training. The precision level attained in KASP was entirely satisfactory for the group analyses in this report. Furthermore, it should be stressed that reported TEMs are an average across measurers of individual TEMs. They are therefore representative of group TEMs rather than individual or interobserver TEMs (undoubtedly lower than those for the team). In assessing individual physique status and in monitoring change, it is prudent to replicate all measures and use the median of three values to assure precision. Accuracy requires explicit definition of landmarks and techniques, absolute adherence to these through formal training, a plan for repeating measures, and the services of an experienced criterion anthropometrist to monitor other measurers.

References

Araujo, C.G.S., Pavel, R.C., & Gomes, P.S.C. (1978). Comparison of somatotype and speed in competitive swimming at different phases of training. In J. Terauds & E.W. Beddingfield (Eds.), *Swimming III* (pp. 329-337). Baltimore: University Park Press.

Bale, P. (1986). The relationship of somatotype and body composition to strength in a group of men and women sport science students. In J.A.P. Day (Ed.), *Perspectives in kinanthropometry* (pp. 187-197). Champaign, IL: Human Kinetics.

Beers, Y. (1957). *Introduction to the theory of error.* Reading, MA: Addison-Wesley.

Bloomfield, J., Blanksby, B.A., Ackland, T.R., & Elliot, B.C. (1986). The anatomical and physiological characteristics of preadolescent swimmers. In J.A.P. Day (Ed.), *Perspectives in kinanthropometry* (pp. 165-170). Champaign, IL: Human Kinetics.

Borms, J., Hebbelinck, M., Carter, J.E.L., Ross, W.D., & Lariviere, G. (1979). Standardization of basic anthropometry in Olympic athletes. In V. Novotny & S. Titlbachova (Eds.), *Methods of functional anthropology* (pp. 31-39). Prague: Charles University.

Brief, F.K. (1986). *Somatotipo y caracteristicas antropometricas de los atletas Bolivarianos.* [Somatotype and anthropometric characteristics of Bolivarian athletes]. Caracas: Universidad Central de Venezuela.

Carr, R.V., Blade, L.F., Rempell, R., & Ross, W.D. (1993). Direct versus proportional lengths: Conceptions and methodological differences. *American Journal of Physical Anthropology,* **90**, 515-517.

Carter, J.E.L. (1970). The somatotypes of athletes: A review. *Human Biology,* **42**, 535-569.

Carter, J.E.L. (Ed.) (1982a). *Physical structure of Olympic athletes. Part I. The Montreal Olympic Games anthropological project.* Basel, Switzerland: Karger.

Carter, J.E.L. (1982b). Body composition of Montreal Olympic athletes. In J.E.L. Carter (Ed.), *Physical structure of Olympic athletes. Part I. The Montreal Olympic Games anthropological project* (pp. 107-116). Basel, Switzerland: Karger.

Carter, J.E.L. (Ed.) (1984a). *Physical structure of Olympic athletes. Part II. Kinanthropometry of Olympic athletes.* Basel, Switzerland: Karger.

Carter, J.E.L. (1984b). Somatotypes of Olympic athletes from 1948 to 1976. In J.E.L. Carter (Ed.), *Physical structure of Olympic athletes. Part II. Kinanthropometry of Olympic athletes* (pp. 80-109). Basel, Switzerland: Karger.

Carter, J.E.L., Aubry, S.P., & Sleet, D.A. (1982a). Somatotypes of Montreal Olympic athletes. In J.E.L. Carter (Ed.), *Physical structure of Olympic athletes. Part I. The Montreal Olympic Games anthropological project* (pp. 53-80). Basel, Switzerland: Karger.

Carter, J.E.L., & Heath, B.H. (1990). *Somatotyping—development and applications.* Cambridge: Cambridge University Press.

Carter, J.E.L., Ross, W.D., Aubry, S.P., Hebbelinck, M., & Borms, J. (1982b). Anthropometry of Montreal Olympic athletes. In J.E.L. Carter (Ed.), *Physical structure of Olympic athletes. Part I. The Montreal Olympic Games anthropological project* (pp. 25-52). Basel, Switzerland: Karger.

Carter, J.E.L., Ross, W.D., Duquet, W., & Aubry, S.P. (1983). Advances in somatotype methodology and analysis. *Yearbook of Physical Anthropology,* **26**, 193-213.

Carter, J.E.L., & Yuhasz, M.S. (1984). Skinfolds and body composition of Olympic athletes. In J.E.L. Carter (Ed.), *Physical structure of Olympic athletes. Part II. Kinanthropometry of Olympic athletes* (pp. 144-182). Basel, Switzerland: Karger.

Changalur, S.N., & Brown, P.L. (1992). An analysis of male and female Olympic swimmers in the 200-meter events. *Canadian Journal of Sport Science,* **17**(2), 104-109.

Clarys, J.P., & Borms, J. (1971). Typologische studie van waterpolospelers en gymnasten [A typological study of water polo players and gymnasts]. *Genueskunde en sport,* **4**, 1, 2-8.

Clarys, J.P., Martin, A.D., & Drinkwater, D.T. (1984). Gross tissue weights in the human body by cadaver dissection. *Human Biology*, **56**(3), 459-473.

Cureton, T.K., Jr. (1951). *Physical fitness of champion athletes*. Urbana, IL: University of Illinois Press.

Day, J.A.P. (1984). Bilateral symmetry and reliability of upper limb measurements. In J.A.P. Day (Ed.), *Perspectives in kinanthropometry* (pp. 257-261). Champaign, IL: Human Kinetics.

Day, J.A.P. (1986). The reliability and bilateral symmetry of the upper limbs: The last word. In T. Reilly, J. Watson, & J. Borms (Eds.), *Kinanthropometry III* (pp. 109-113). London: E. & F.N. Spon.

de Garay, A.L., Levine, L., & Carter, J.E.L. (1974). *Genetic and anthropological studies of Olympic athletes*. New York: Academic Press.

Francis, P.R., & Welshons-Smith, K. (1982). A preliminary investigation of the support scull in synchronized swimming using a video motion analysis system. In J. Terauds (Ed.), *Biomechanics in sport* (pp. 401-407). Del Mar, CA: Academic.

Grimston, S.K., & Hay, J.G. (1986). Relationships among anthropometric and stroking characteristics of college swimmers. *Medicine and Science in Sports and Exercise*, **18**(1), 60-68.

Hawes, M.R., & Sovak, D. (1993). Skeletal ruggedness as a factor in performance of Olympic and national calibre synchronised swimmers. In W. Duquet & J.A.P. Day (Eds.), *Kinanthropometry IV*. London: E. & F.N. Spon.

Hebbelinck, M., Carter, L., & de Garay, A. (1975). Body build and somatotype of Olympic swimmers, divers, and water polo players. In L. Lewillie & J.P. Clarys (Eds.), *Swimming II* (pp. 285-305). Baltimore: University Park Press.

Heinrich, C.H., Going, S.B., Pamenter, R.W., Boyden, T.W., & Lohman, T.G. (1990). Bone mineral density of cyclically menstruating female resistance and endurance trained athletes. *Medicine and Science in Sports and Exercise*, **22**(5), 558-563.

Hrdlicka, A. (1952). *Practical anthropometry* (4th ed.). Philadelphia: Wistar Institute of Anatomy and Biology.

Huijing, P.A., Toussaint, H.M., Mackay, R., Vervoorn, K., Clarys, J.P., de Groot, G., & Hollander, A.P. (1988). Active drag related to body dimensions. In B.E. Ungerechts, K. Reischle, & K. Wilke (Eds.), *Swimming science V*, (pp. 31-38). Champaign, IL: Human Kinetics.

Jungmann, H. (Ed.) (1976). *Sportwissenschaftliche Untersuchungen wahrend der XX Olympischen Spiele, Munchen 1972* [A sport science investigation during the 20th Olympic Games, Munich 1972]. Grafelfing.

Kirkendall, D.T., Delio, D.J., Hagerman, G.R., & Fox, E.T. (1982). Body composition of elite and intermediate class synchronized swimmers. *Synchro*, **20**(6), 10-11.

Leek, G.M. (1968). The physiques of New Zealand water polo players. *New Zealand Journal of Health, Physical Education and Recreation*, **3** (Nov.), 39-47.

Leek, G.M. (1969). The physique of swimming champions. *New Zealand Journal of Health, Physical Education and Recreation*, **2**(3), 30-41.

Lohman, T.G., Roche, A.F., & Martorell, R. (1988). *Anthropometric standardization reference manual*. Champaign, IL: Human Kinetics.

Lohman, T.G., Slaughter, M.H., Boileau, R.A., Bunt, J.C., & Lussier, L. (1984). Bone mineral content measurements and their relation to body density in children, youth, and adults. *Human Biology*, **56**, 677-679.

Maglischo, E.W. (1982). *Swimming faster*. Palo Alto, CA: Mayfield.

Martin, A.D. (1991). Anthropometric assessment of bone mineral. In J. Himes (Ed.), *Anthropometric assessment of nutritional status* (pp. 185-196). New York: Wiley-Liss.

Martin, A.D., Spenst, L.F., Drinkwater, D.T., & Clarys, J.P. (1990). Anthropometric estimation of muscle mass in men. *Medicine and Science in Sports and Exercise*, **22**(5), 729-733.

Martin, R., & Saller, K. (1957). *Lehrbuch der Anthropologie* (Vol. 1) [Handbook of anthropology (Vol. 1)]. Stuttgart, Germany: Fischer.

Matiegka, J. (1921). The testing of physical efficiency. *American Journal of Physical Anthropology, 4,* 223-230.

Mazza, J.C., Alarcon, N., Galasso, C., Bermudez, C., Cosolito, P., & Gribaudo, F. (1991b). Proportionality and anthropometric fractionation of body mass in South American swimmers. In J.M. Cameron (Ed.), *Aquatic sports medicine* (pp. 230-244). London: Farrand Press.

Mazza, J.C., Cosolito, P., Alarcon, N., Galasso, C., Bermudez, C., Gribaudo, G., & Feretti, J.L. (1991a). Somatotype profile of South American Swimmers. In T. Reilly, A. Lees, M. Hughes, & D. MacLaren (Eds.), *Biomechanics and Medicine in Swimming* (pp. 371-378). Georgetown, ON, Canada: Routledge, Chapman & Hall, Inc.Moffat, R., Katch, V.L., Freedson, P., & Lindeman, J. (1980). Body composition of synchronized swimmers. *Canadian Journal of Applied Sports Sciences, 5*(3), 153-155.

Novak, L.P., Bestit, C., Mellerowicz, H., & Woodward, W.A. (1976a). Maximal oxygen consumption, body composition and anthropometry of selected Olympic male athletes. In H. Jungmann (Ed.), *Sportwissenschaftliche Untersuchungen wahrend der XX Olympischen Spiele, Munchen 1972* (pp. 57-68). Grafelfing, Germany: Demeter.

Novak, L.P., Woodward, W.A., Bestit, C., & Mellerowicz, H. (1976b). Working capacity (WC 170), body composition and anthropometry of Olympic female athletes. In H. Jungmann (Ed.), *Sportwissenschaftliche Untersuchungen wahrend der XX Olympischen Spiele, Munchen 1972* (pp. 69-78). Grafelfing, Germany: Demeter.

Packard, G.C., & Boardman, T.J. (1988). The misuse of ratios, indices and percentages in ecophysiological research. *Physiological Zoology, 61,* 1-9.

Parnell, R.W. (1958). *Behaviour and physique.* London: Edward Arnold.

Perez, B. (1981). *Los atletas Venezolanos, su tipo fisico* [Venezuelan athletes, their physique type]. Caracas: Universidad Central de Venezuela.

Poole, G.W., Crepin, B.J., & Sevigny, M. (1980). Physiological characteristics of elite synchronized swimmers. *Canadian Journal of Applied Sport Sciences, 5*(3), 156-160.

Risser, W.L., Lee, E.J., LeBlanc, A., Poindexter, H.B., Risser, J.M., & Schneider, V. (1990). Bone density in eumenorrheic female college athletes. *Medicine and Science in Sports and Exercise, 22*(5), 570-574.

Rocha, M.L., de Araujo, C.G.S., de Freitas, J., & Villasboas, L.F.P. (1977). Anthropometria dinamica da Natacao [Dynamic anthropometry in swimming]. *Revista de Educacao Fisica, Brasil, 102,* 46-54.

Rodriguez, C., Sanchez, G., Garcia, E., Martinez, M., & Cabrera, T. (1986). Contribucion al estudio del perfil morfologico de atletas cubanos de alto rendimiento, del sexo masculino [Contribution to the study of the morphological profile of highly competitive male Cuban athletes]. *Boletin Cientifico-tecnico, Inder Cuba, 1/2,* 6-24.

Ross, W.D., Corlett, J.T., Drinkwater, D.T., Faulkner, R., & Vajda, A. (1977, September). *Anthropometry of synchronized swimmers.* Unpublished proceedings, Canadian Association of Sports Sciences Symposium, Winnipeg, Canada.

Ross, W.D., De Rose, E.H., & Ward, R. (1988). Anthropometry applied to sports medicine. In A. Dirix, H.G. Knuttgen, & T.K. Tittel (Eds.), *The Olympic book of sports medicine* (pp. 233-265). Oxford: Blackwell.

Ross, W.D., Marfell-Jones, M.F., & Stirling, D.R. (1982). Prospects in kinanthropometry. In J.J. Jackson & H.A. Wenger (Eds.), *The sports sciences* (Physical Education Series No. 4) (pp. 134-150). Victoria, BC: University of Victoria Press.

Ross, W.D., & Marfell-Jones, M.J. (1991). Kinanthropometry. In J.D. MacDougall, H.A. Wenger, & H.J. Green (Eds.), *Physiological testing of the high-performance athlete* (pp. 233-308). Champaign, IL: Human Kinetics.

Ross, W.D., & Wilson, N.C. (1974). A strategem for proportional growth assessment. In J. Borms & M. Hebbelinck (Eds.), *Acta Pediatrica Belgica* (Suppl. 28), 169-182.

Ross, W.D., Ward, R., Leahy, R.M., & Day, J.A.P. (1984). Proportionality of Montreal Olympic athletes. In J.E.L. Carter (Ed.), *Physical structure of Olympic athletes. Part I. The Montreal Olympic games anthropological project* (pp. 81-106). Basel, Switzerland: Karger.

SPSS, Inc. (1990). *SPSS Base System User's Guide*. Chicago: SPSS.

Stager, J.M., Cordain, L., & Becker, T.J. (1984). Relationship of body composition to swimming performance in female swimmers. *Journal of Swimming Research, 1*, 21-26.

Tanner, J.M. (1949). Fallacy of per-weight and per-surface area standards and their relation to spurious correlation. *Journal of Applied Physiology, 2*, 1-15.

Thorland, W.G., Johnson, G.O., Fagot, T.G., Tharp, G.D., & Hammer, R.W. (1981). Body composition and somatotype characteristics of junior Olympic athletes. *Medicine and Science in Sports and Exercise, 13*, 332-338.

Tittel, K., & Wutscherk, H. (1972). *Sportanthropometrie* [Sport an anthropometry]. Leipzig, Germany: Barth.

Topping, J. (1962). *Errors of observation and their treatment* (3rd ed.). London: Chapman & Hall.

Toussaint, H.M., de Looze, M., van Rossem, B., Leijdekkers, M., & Dignum, H. (1990). The effect of growth on drag in young swimmers. *International Journal of Sport Biomechanics, 6*, 18-28.

Vervaeke, H., & Persyn, U. (1981). Some differences between men and women in various factors which determine swimming performance. In J. Borms, M. Hebbelinck, & A. Venerando (Eds.), *The female athlete* (pp. 150-156). Basel, Switzerland: Karger.

Ward, R. (1988). *The O-Scale system for human physique assessment*. Unpublished doctoral dissertation, Simon Fraser University, Burnaby, Canada.

Weiner, J.S., & Lourie, J.A. (1981). *Practical human biology*. London: Academic Press.

Withers, R.T., Craig, N.P., & Norton, K.I. (1986). Somatotypes of South Australian male athletes. *Human Biology, 58*, 337-356.

Zeng, L. (1985). *The morphological characteristics of elite Chinese athletes who participated in gymnastics, swimming, weightlifting and track and field events*. Unpublished master's thesis, State University of New York, Cortland.

About the Editors

J.E. Lindsay Carter is professor emeritus in the Department of Physical Education at San Diego State University (SDSU). He joined the university in 1962 and taught applied anatomy, biomechanics, and kinanthropometry before retiring in 1993. Before his work at SDSU, he was a research assistant, lecturer, and assistant professor at the University of Otago in his native New Zealand.

Carter holds a PhD in physical education from the University of Iowa, which he attended as a Fulbright Scholar from 1956 to 1959. He has written extensively on the related aspects of physique and performance, kinanthropometry, and exercise science, having authored 2 books, 18 book chapters, and 71 scholarly articles as well as having edited 4 books.

Dr. Carter's honors include being elected Fellow of the American Academy of Physical Education in 1982 and being presented the Outstanding Faculty Award by San Diego State University in 1983. He has served as vice president of the International Society for the Advancement of Kinanthropometry and is a member of the American College of Sports Medicine.

Timothy Ackland is a senior lecturer in the Department of Human Movement at the University of Western Australia (UWA) in Perth. He has been affiliated with the school, first as a student and then as a staff member, since 1976. As a student at UWA, Ackland earned a BPE in 1980, an MPE in 1982, and a PhD in biomechanics in 1988. As an employee of the school, Ackland began as a coordinator and research assistant in 1981 and worked his way through the ranks. He held the positions of tutor, lecturer, senior tutor, and tenured lecturer before becoming a tenured senior lecturer in 1993.

Dr. Ackland has written numerous articles on biomechanics, human growth and development, and sport science and is a co-author of *Athletics, Growth and Development in Children: The University of Western Australia Study.* In 1989, he was given the Distinguished Teacher Award by the University of Western Australia, and in 1992 he was presented the Australian Sports Medicine Federation Fellows' Young Investigator Award. Ackland is a member of the Australian Association for Exercise and Sport Science and the International Society for the Advancement of Kinanthropometry.